# GREAT BRITISH
# MARINE ANIMALS

### PAUL NAYLOR

This book is dedicated to Teresa, with thanks for all her positive ideas and endless encouragement

## Acknowledgements

I am very grateful to Steve Carpenter at Sound Diving for his continued support and to Emily, Ellie and Sam for their inspiration. Special thanks also go to Alan Hodgson and Hazel Gooch for providing drawings, to Tom Alderson, Seb Shimeld, Ann Beeby, Nigel Smallbones, Clare Howard, Mary Simmons and Ron Bird for putting so much effort into commenting on the text and to Keith Hiscock for valuable advice on some of the photographs. I would also like to acknowledge those people without whose help I would never have got many of the photographs. These include John Baldry, Tim Nicholson, Lyndon Taylor, Mark Perrott, Les Kemp, Bill Bowen, Sue Scott, Mark Buddles, Cilla Course, Porthkerris Divers, Undersea Adventures and many others.

## The author

Paul Naylor has been snorkelling and diving around the coast of Britain for nearly 30 years. Whether in the muddy shallows of a beach lagoon in Norfolk or in the deep and clear water around the Orkneys, he has always been entranced by the animals that live there. For the last 20 years, Paul has concentrated on photographing these animals in their natural habitat and, wherever possible, showing them getting on with their lives despite his attention. He gives talks to schools, colleges, conservation groups and diving clubs on the wonders of our marine fauna; and writes regularly about marine life for diving magazines and other publications. He has a doctorate in marine biology and is an Associate of the Royal Photographic Society.

Published by
**SOUND DIVING**
PUBLICATIONS

First Published 2003

ISBN 0 9522831 4 X

Sales or other enquiries, including requests for photographs:
telephone 07041 351307 (local rate)
or visit www.marinephoto.co.uk

Printed by Deltor: 01752 841717

# CONTENTS

Front cover photographs: Cuckoo wrasse (female),
long-clawed squat lobster, jewel anemones

Page 1: Tompot blenny

Diver in a rock gully lined with soft corals and sea anemones, St Abbs

# Chapter 1
# INTRODUCTION
## Britain's colourful and fascinating creatures

The undersea world that surrounds Britain is home to the most wonderful array of marine animals. Not only are many of these animals amazingly colourful in the strict visual sense of their appearance, they also lead remarkably colourful lives in terms of their intriguing and bizarre habits. Many people, on first seeing photographs of our native marine animals, think they are looking at pictures taken in an exotic tropical location, and take some convincing that all these creatures are actually living in British waters! There is tremendous variety, with several thousand species including representatives from all the major animal groups. Best of all, it isn't even necessary to wear complex diving gear and explore great depths to enjoy this profusion of life. Diving is certainly an excellent way to watch these animals, but many can be seen while snorkelling close to shore or exploring rock pools without even getting wet.

I have been enthralled by Britain's native marine animals for nearly 30 years and this book, my most ambitious yet, has been written in an attempt to share my fascination and enthusiasm for them.

### About this book

This book is intended to serve several purposes. While designed to aid identification of the common animals of British seas, it also incorporates as much material as possible showing how the animals go about their lives. There is information on how they feed, breed, avoid becoming someone else's food, and interact with other species in different ways. Above all, I hope it demonstrates what beautiful and fascinating creatures inhabit the sea that surrounds us.

It is the third book arising from my interest in marine animals. The first two were called "Marine Animals of the South West" and were based mainly on my diving experience in that part of Britain. My aim, particularly in the greatly improved second edition, was to introduce as much information on behaviour as possible. Many people liked this approach but some expressed disappointment that the book didn't "cover" the whole of Britain. *Great British Marine Animals* has been written with them in mind, after doing a lot more diving and photography around the rest of Britain. Many species, only found in the other areas or more common there, are now included. In addition, the material on some species covered in the previous books has been expanded, with new photographs showing different aspects of their lives.

### An important message

By showing the beauty and intriguing nature of animals living around our coasts, I hope this book

Profusion of animal life, including sponges, sea anemones, hydroids, tube-worms, top-shells, bryozoans, sea squirts and fish on a current-swept reef in Plymouth Sound

helps to demonstrate the importance of conserving the habitats in which they can thrive. Too many people seem to think our seas are grey and uninteresting, a view which can only reinforce an attitude of indifference to what we put in to (and take out of) them. All of the world's oceans and their inhabitants are under pressure from a variety of environmental threats. The cool northern rim of the Atlantic needs our care and attention in just the same way as does the warm splendour of coral seas.

## Animal classification

There is a complicated scientific classification system for living things but I have tried to refer to it as little as possible in this book. However, the term "phylum" (plural: "phyla") will keep cropping up. A phylum is the broadest sub-division of the animal kingdom. Phyla make useful categories and it is these that have formed, roughly speaking, the remaining chapters of this book. I say roughly, because animals from more than one phylum are described as worms (Chapter 4) while sea squirts (Chapter 9) and fish (Chapter 10) belong to the same phylum. Further subdivisions of phyla are discussed in the relevant chapters. Out of all the animals in this book, only the fish have a proper backbone and are classified as vertebrates. All the rest are invertebrates.

A huge array of animal species, from many different groups, can be seen in a small area. Between them, the two photographs on this double page contain representatives from every major animal phylum. The photograph from Plymouth Sound, above, shows sponges (Chapter 2), sea anemones (Chapter 3), coral worms (Chapter 4), top-shells (Chapter 6), a turf of bryozoans (Chapter 7), sea squirts (Chapter 9) and small goldsinny wrasse (Chapter 10) all in close proximity. The photograph from a sea loch near Oban on the opposite page contains a shore crab (Chapter 5), brittle stars (Chapter 8) and further worms, sponges and sea squirts.

Shore crab, brittle stars, sponges and sea squirts living amongst *Serpula* worm tubes near Oban

This diver has spotted a cuttlefish buried in the sandy seabed

Latin terms have been kept to an absolute minimum in the book, apart from including the Latin name for individual animal species. Latin species names are undoubtedly useful, partly because many common animals (various sponges, sea anemones, sea slugs and sea squirts for example) have no English name. Latin names are also unambiguous and precise but it should be noted that they are not always constant. The velvet swimming crab has had four different Latin names over the last thirty years, while still being called the velvet swimming crab. A Latin name comes in two parts: the first part denotes the genus (the narrowest classification sub-division before species) and the second part the species. Very similar animals belong to the same genus, in which case they will have the same first name; totally different animals may have the same second name because it can simply mean "common" or "red" for example. The combination of the two refers to a single species

and gives an animal a unique label. The Latin name of the cuckoo wrasse, for example, is *Labrus bimaculatus* and the closely related ballan wrasse, *Labrus bergylta*, belongs to the same genus.

## Using the book

It is very difficult to draw up rules for identifying animals. Key features in one group may be irrelevant in another. The best option is probably to scan through the photographs looking for similar creatures to the one seen, and then refer to the text for more detail. Colour, size and the habitat where it is found can all give clues to an animal's identity but can also mislead. Information on colour and habitat is given as appropriate, while an idea of approximate size is given for all species in an attempt to put the photographs into perspective. The size given for each species is very much a maximum so the majority of individuals seen may be considerably

Diver exploring the wreck of the Hispania near Mull. The wreck is festooned with sea anemones, soft corals and other animals

smaller. It is also possible, however, that the occasional specimen is even larger. The reader may find the number of descriptions preceded by "often", "usually" and "commonly" frustrating but omitting these words would give a false idea of precision and certainty.

Many of the animal species in this book are found all around Britain where there is suitable habitat. Notes on distribution are usually only included where there is good agreement between reference books that distribution is restricted. I have also included a few of my own observations on distribution where they seem to be relevant.

## The animal species covered in this book

This book is far from comprehensive in the species it covers. If expanded to include each of the nearly 7,000 species of marine animal in British seas, it would run to about 30 volumes the size of this one. I have tried to include the most

frequently seen and obvious animals, while providing a selection from each group that gives an idea of the types of creatures they contain. More familiar animals are covered in more detail. The sections on fish, starfish and crabs, for instance, are more wide-ranging (though still far from exhaustive) than those on sponges and sea squirts. In any case, I have deliberately taken up space to show common animals (hermit crabs, cuttlefish, starfish for example) going about their lives, in preference to including less familiar animals sitting still. Where text on a species runs over more than one page, key words are **highlighted** to make information easier to find. For more thorough identification of a greater number of species, books with more detail should be consulted (see page 224). Some of these books concentrate on animals within a specific group.

## Different habitats

A few glimpses of the undersea world will confirm that different habitats support very

Sunlit intertidal shallows with seaweed, barnacles and limpets, St Abbs

Reef (at 12 m) covered in sea anemones and sponges with kelp growing on top of the rocks, Skye

Animal-dominated scenery in deep water (25 m) off Cornwall; soft corals, bryozoans, a sea urchin and a female cuckoo wrasse

different communities of animals. Numerous factors play a part but two of the most important are the type of seabed and the depth of water.

Rocky seabeds tend to support the most obvious and colourful forms of life and are therefore usually preferred for snorkelling and diving activities. Sandy or muddy seabeds can appear desolate by comparison but still house many wonderful creatures. It is just that many of them burrow down and spend most of their time out of view (see photograph of cuttlefish on page 8). Shipwrecks (see photograph on page 9) are extremely popular dive sites because, aside from their historic interest, they are wonderfully rich habitats. These "man-made reefs" provide shelter for animals that like to hide away (crabs, lobsters, some fish), and also act as raised anchorage points for those that rely on filtering their food from seawater as it flows past (sea anemones, corals, fan worms).

The depth of water over a habitat has a profound effect on its characteristics because, among other things, it determines how much light there is to support the growth of seaweed. The three pictures on this double page show the effect of different depths and light levels. The first photograph is taken in the tidal shallows where bright sunlight can penetrate. Here the scenery is dominated by seaweed and animals (such as barnacles and limpets) that can tolerate being exposed to air when the tide goes out. The second photograph was taken in about 12 metres of water. Seaweed (kelp) is growing on the very tops of the rocks where there is enough light but, down the shady sides of the reef, seaweed cannot thrive and the rock is covered in animals such as sponges and sea anemones. There is not enough light at 25 metres for much seaweed at all and the scenery is generally dominated by animals as shown in the third photograph. Here, dead men's fingers, sea fans (both are soft corals) and

Tompot blenny found near a shipwreck in very shallow water

Ross coral (a bryozoan, not a coral) are thriving. The depth also means that these fairly delicate creatures receive little stress from the pounding of waves when the sea is rough.

## Finding and watching Britain's marine animals

Wherever conditions are suitable for looking in shore pools, or for snorkelling or diving, marine animals can be seen, often in great profusion. Snorkelling in just a few metres of water off a beach can reveal all sorts of wonders, particularly if there is varied scenery including both rocky and sandy habitats. Have a close-up look at those barnacles; when submerged, their feeding limbs sweep out from the tops of their shells like grasping hands in miniature. Small shannies may be watched trying to bite off the limbs while keeping a wary eye for predatory fish such as bass sweeping in through the shallows. Crabs can be seen looking around for food too, assuming their defensive claws-spread posture if approached too closely. Around deeper rocks, but still while just snorkelling, beautifully coloured wrasse and appealing tompot blennies (see above) may be found. Interesting aspects of behaviour can also be observed in the shallowest water. Rock cook wrasse are well known for cleaning larger fish,

Rock cook wrasse attempting to "clean" a spider crab

but one found close to a beach and shown here (above) was attempting to remove encrusting growth from a large spider crab. As the crab's attachments serve as camouflage, the rock cook's services were probably not welcome! There are descriptions of animal behaviour throughout the book. Species that give particularly good examples of co-operation, courtship, hunting, camouflage etc. are listed on pages 228-229.

Whether rockpooling, snorkelling or diving, it is important that our activities don't harm the animals we are watching. On the shore, this means replacing any rocks turned over exactly as we found them and generally treading gently. Underwater, it means watching where we put our hands, knees and particularly our fins. It is very important for underwater photographers to avoid damaging fragile marine life when concentrating on manoeuvering into a good position for taking a picture. Failure to do this makes us the undersea equivalent of the most aggressive paparazzi!

## Photography

Virtually all the photographs in this book were taken underwater, portraying animals in their natural habitat. Aside from the obvious cases of the cuttlebone and discarded crab shells, the only exceptions are the sea anemone feeding (page 25), the mussel with foot extended (page 126), the little cuttle (page 135), the cod (page 186) and the rock goby (page 217), which were taken in an aquarium. All the photographs were taken on Fuji Velvia slide film. I use Nikon 801 land cameras, with 60 mm or 105 mm macro lenses and a 20 mm wide-angle lens, in dedicated aluminium housings from Subal. Lighting is by electronic flashguns from Sea and Sea (a single YS300 or two small YS50's) and Inon (Z-22 Quad flash). A few shots in the book were taken with a Nikonos III, 15 mm lens and single flashgun. There are many different options for underwater photographic equipment, but I would recommend all the above items for their excellent reliability and performance over many years of hard use.

# Chapter 2
# SPONGES

## Simple creatures

Apart from minute creatures that consist of a single cell, like amoeba, sponges are the simplest members of the animal kingdom. Their cells are specialised for different functions, such as feeding, support or reproduction, but they do not form complex structures like the cells of higher animals. There are no digestive, nervous or circulatory systems for example. The lack of sophistication in sponges has been demonstrated by famous experiments where, having been broken down by being pushed through fine silk, they soon succeed in reassembling themselves. Because sponges are completely static, they were at one time thought to be plants.

## Living filters

Sponges are effectively animated filters and their phylum name, Porifera, means "pore bearer". Water is drawn into the sponge's central cavity through its pores, the numerous tiny holes all over its body surface, and leaves by the outlet vents which are much larger, more obvious and fewer in number than the inlet pores. Special cells within the sponge create the water current with continuously beating cilia (tiny whip-like hairs), and collect suspended food particles that are sucked in. This mechanism is simple but effective, and a sponge only a few centimetres across can filter over 20 litres of seawater in a day.

## Reproduction

Sponges can reproduce by asexual processes such as budding, or by sexual means. Most sponges are hermaphrodite (simultaneously male and female) but eggs and sperm from the same sponge mature at different times so it does not fertilise itself. Sperm leaves with the outgoing water current, drifts off to fertilise the eggs in other sponges and free-swimming larvae are produced. The larvae then settle and, if the habitat is right, grow into new sponges.

## Support and defence

Sponges are supported by a rudimentary skeleton composed of spicules, protein fibres or both. The spicules are needle-like or branched spiky structures made from calcium or silicon compounds. In tropical sponges, it is their fibrous skeleton that produces a traditional bath sponge when the other constituents are stripped away. In addition to providing support, the sharp spicules help to make sponges unpalatable. Many species also produce unpleasant tasting chemicals to deter predators, as any other escape response is beyond their capabilities.

# Sea orange - *Suberites ficus*

Also known as the sulphur sponge, the sea orange is a classic example of the archetypal sponge. It forms quite large rounded masses that have an even but slightly rough surface, which represents the vast number of tiny pores through which water is pumped into the sponge. In every mass, there is at least one large circular opening through which water is pumped out again. It is easy to peer into one of these openings and see something of the sponge's internal structure. Colour is usually orange but can be brownish or yellow. The sea orange is most common on rocks and stones where there is some mud present, and can also be found growing on the shells inhabited by hermit crabs. Here, it may completely enclose the hermit's shell and, if this eventually dissolves, the sponge will form the crab's replacement home. [Up to 20 cm across]

# Boring sponge - *Cliona celata*

An obvious mass of the yellow sponge

The name of this sponge arises, not from its uninteresting nature, but from the fact that it bores its way into soft rock such as that of limestone reefs. In many instances, most of the sponge is hidden within a network of passages and chambers that it has excavated in the substrate. All that is visible on the seabed are then the characteristic yellow "studs" and vents (see smallest photograph) where water enters and leaves the sponge respectively. Sometimes, however, the sponge outgrows its chambers and can form

Here, only the vents are visible

large, very obvious masses, which are still covered in the familiar "studs" and vents. The main photograph on this page shows such a mass, surrounded by trumpet anemones (page 36) and the photograph opposite shows a particularly extensive growth. The sponge's boring process is chemical, and employs an acid by-product of respiration. Special cells use this process to undercut and surround tiny pieces of rock which are then "spat out" with the water flow. The sponge also bores into the shells of molluscs and can be a serious pest in commercial oyster beds. [Masses can reach up to 1 m across but are usually much smaller]

Boring sponge - *Cliona celata*

Extensive growth of boring sponge on a reef near the Lizard, Cornwall

## *Polymastia mamillaris*

At first sight, this species does not really look like a typical sponge and could almost be mistaken for a colonial sea squirt. It is often found in quite silty locations and the sponge's cushion-like base may be obscured by a covering of sediment so only a forest of projections is visible, as in the photograph.

Some of these projections have pointed tips while others are open-ended tubes like miniature chimneys; all are usually creamy-white and translucent. [Base of sponge up to 15 cm across, "chimneys" up to 10 cm tall but usually far smaller]

## *Raspailia ramosa*

Colonies of this sponge resemble small dense bushes, with the "branches" having rounded and slightly bulbous ends. Its colouration is an attractive dark reddish-brown that can appear almost crimson under torch-light. However, fine silt often adheres to its

velvety surface layer and obscures this rich colour. Small water outlet openings can be seen scattered across the surface of the branches. ["Bushes" up to 15 cm tall]

## *Axinella dissimilis*

A distinctively shaped sponge which is usually found in quite deep and clear water offshore. Its orange or yellow fan-like form stands erect from rock faces. The branches, which may be joined for part of their length, are flattened and therefore oval in cross-section, with

rounded ends. The overall shape is slightly reminiscent of the sea fan (page 53). While totally different types of animal, their form presumably serves the same function in both cases: to maximise the surface area that comes into contact with food-bearing currents. [Up to 15 cm tall]

## *Axinella infundibuliformis*

This off-white or beige sponge has a very characteristic form and is usually shaped like a funnel or shallow wine glass. The cup is attached to the rock, on which it lives, by a short stalk or stem. The rim of this cup is thick and rounded. The surface of the sponge is fairly smooth and the numerous water outlet

holes spread evenly across it are clearly visible. Even though it is often found on quite silty rocks, the sponge's cup generally appears clean. White and orange dead men's fingers (pages 50-51) can be seen beside the sponge in the photograph. [Cup up to 25 cm across but often much smaller]

## Breadcrumb sponge - *Halichondria panicea*

A very common encrusting sponge that can form large sheets or lumps on rocks in shallow water, often beneath overhangs. The sheets may be thin or quite thick, with the raised water outlet holes looking like miniature volcanoes or chimneys. It can occur in a variety of shades, from olive green through a dirty cream to pale yellow. The green colouration is due to algae which live symbiotically within the sponge's tissues, and are dependent on the amount of light available. Breadcrumb sponge found under gloomy overhangs or in deeper water has less algae and is therefore more yellow. [Encrustations can reach over 1 m across and are of very variable thickness]

## Mermaid's glove - *Haliclona oculata*

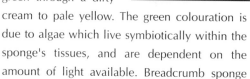

This sponge forms characteristic shrub-like colonies which can grow upwards from a flat seabed or stick out from a vertical rock surface. The branches, which are often numerous, are dirty yellow or beige in colour, have a round cross-section and bear distinct water outlet holes along their length. *Haliclona* can tolerate quite silty conditions and is common in the outer reaches of estuaries. The fish in this photograph, and the one opposite, are goldsinny wrasse (page 208). ["Shrubs" can be up to 30 cm tall, branches 1 cm across]

## Hemimycale columella

Sometimes known as the "crater sponge", the surface of this pale pink, orange or yellow encrusting sponge is indeed covered with characteristic craters. The rims of the craters are particularly obvious because they are paler in shade than the rest of the sponge and this produces a honeycomb pattern. Each of the craters

contains one or more small but visible water outlet holes. This sponge is most common in the south west of Britain. [Encrustations up to 1 cm thick and 30 cm across]

## Esperiopsis fucorum

*Esperiopsis* is an encrusting sponge that can form sheets or mounds. It is usually deep orange in colour, and has a delicate, quite flexible consistency. Under more sheltered conditions, it forms many distinctive long and slender tassels that stick out from the rest of the encrustation.

The large water outlet holes may be scattered over a flat surface of the sponge or raised up like chimneys. It grows with great abundance in many locations such as the Menai Straits and Plymouth Sound. [Encrustations of very variable size, tassels can be 10 cm long]

## Microciona atrasanguinea

The brilliant deep red colour is a distinguishing feature of this sponge and the large patches it forms on rock faces, wrecks or pier legs look like splashes of red paint. These encrustations are only a few millimetres thick and are fairly smooth in comparison with many sponges. Wavy channels in the surface of the sponge converge into water outlet openings to produce a distinctive pattern. [Encrustations up to 30 cm across]

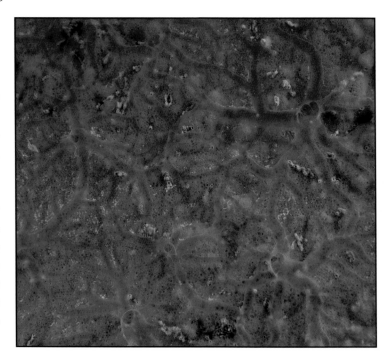

## Elephant's hide sponge  -  *Pachymatisma johnstonia*

The large grey mounds or plates formed by the elephant's hide sponge (also known as the elephant's ear sponge) are usually found protruding from vertical rock faces. Its surfaces are smooth and hard with obvious holes arranged in patches or lines, where water that has passed through the sponge is expelled. Water is taken in through

more numerous and much smaller openings all over the body of the sponge. This photograph shows a typical large growth of the sponge; close to it on the reef are fan worm tubes (page 69), a bloody Henry starfish (page 150) and Devonshire cup corals (page 49). Elephant's hide sponge can sometimes be coloured blue or white (the tompot blenny on page 210 is resting on a growth that is almost white). [Plates of sponge can be over 1 m across but are usually smaller]

## *Scypha ciliata*

A species with a roughly cylindrical shape, rather like a tall, slim vase. The dense cream or brown coloured hairs that cover it produce a distinctive shaggy appearance. It can be found attached to rocks or seaweed, often in small groups. The single water outlet hole is positioned at the free end of the sponge and is surrounded by a ring of longer, stiff hairs. This sponge's body wall is supported by calcium-based spicules and it is classified in a different group from all the preceding species in this chapter, which have silicon-based spicules. [Up to 4 cm long]

## Lace sponge - *Clathrina coriacea*

This sponge has a distinctively mesh-like appearance, as it consists of a mass of delicate interconnecting tubes. Usually white in colour, it forms a very obvious encrusting sheet over rock surfaces. It is often found living with the red gooseberry sea squirt (see page 174) as it is in this photograph. The water inlet and outlet holes of this species are too small to see with the naked eye. Like *Scypha ciliata* (above), the skeleton of this sponge is based on compounds of calcium rather than silicon. [Encrustations up to 1 cm thick; irregular in outline but up to 20 cm across]

# Chapter 3

# CNIDARIANS

## Sea anemones, corals, hydroids & jellyfish

## Armed and dangerous

The distinguishing feature of cnidarians is that they have stinging cells. These cells contain discharge capsules, called cnidae, that give the group its name. The discharge capsules, which are used for both defence and the capture of prey, are impressive examples of engineering in miniature. Each capsule contains a long hollow, coiled thread which uncoils and shoots out under water pressure when the cell is triggered by touch or chemical stimulus. Different threads have varied functions and, when thousands are triggered together, they can have a powerful effect. Some simply entangle the prey, while others stick to it or inject poison. Some even have blades that, in combination with the twisting action of the threads, act as tiny drills on the armoured surfaces of small crustaceans.

A discharge capsule (cnida) before and after discharge.

## A step up from sponges

Apart from their exceptional weapon system, cnidarians are fairly simple animals. They have different tissues specialised for various functions, so they are a step up from the sponges, but they do not have proper organs like higher invertebrates. There is no true circulation system and only an extremely simple nerve network. Their tentacles, covered in dense batteries of stinging cells, capture prey animals and pass them to the central mouth where they are engulfed - see photographs (opposite) of a beadlet anemone swallowing a shrimp that it has caught. There is no anus so the mouth is also used for the expulsion of undigested material.

## Polyps and medusae – their role in the different groups

Cnidarians can occur in the form of either a polyp, living anchored to the seabed, or a free-swimming medusa.

Sea anemones only occur in the polyp form. These flower-like animals are almost always found attached to rocks or other hard surfaces. Water pressure inside the body maintains the anemone's shape and provides a base for muscle action. They reproduce by producing eggs which normally develop into new adults via a

The beadlet anemone at the top is eating a shrimp

......a few minutes later

planktonic (floating) larval stage. Asexual reproduction may also occur where an adult anemone splits or buds to form a new individual and dense colonies can result.

The following terms are often used when describing sea anemones:

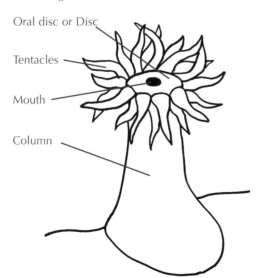

Oral disc or Disc

Tentacles

Mouth

Column

Corals are essentially the same type of animal as sea anemones, occurring only in the polyp form, but they produce some sort of skeleton to support and protect their bodies. Stony corals are usually colonial, their fused chalky skeletons able to form huge coral reefs in tropical waters. Some, including the commonest British species, are completely solitary. In terms of biological classification, the sea anemones and stony corals are very similar and belong to the same sub-group. Within this sub-group there are further anemone-like species such as the burrowing anemones, the encrusting anemones and the jewel anemone which are not classified as "true" anemones. Soft corals, sea fans and sea pens belong to a related but separate sub-group. They are colonial animals whose "mutual" skeleton is not a solid mass of calcium carbonate, but is gelatinous with embedded calcareous or horny spicules imparting strength and some rigidity.

Hydroids, or sea-firs, are the simplest of the stinging-celled animals. Most hydroid species occur in both the polyp and medusa form at different times during their life cycle, but the polyp stage is dominant. The medusa stage may be free swimming or be simply an extension to the polyps. The polyps form colonies where they are linked by strands of living tissue and individuals may serve different functions within the colony. Some polyps, for example, are responsible for feeding while others form the reproductive medusae.

Jellyfish are like hydroids, in usually having both polyp and medusa stages, but it is the medusa stage that dominates as a large floating predator. Its body typically forms a "bell" or "umbrella" which can contract rhythmically to propel the animal through the water. As in all cnidarians, tentacles armed with stinging cells catch prey and pass it to the mouth, so jellyfish can be visualised as floating sea anemones. The diagram below shows a typical jellyfish life cycle. Male jellyfish release sperm into the seawater which is drawn in through the female's mouth and fertilises her eggs. The eggs then develop within the female until swimming larvae are produced. These larvae settle on the seabed and develop into small polyps with long tentacles. The polyps grow and split across so their bodies eventually become a stack of saucer-shaped structures. The "saucers" separate off as miniature jellyfish and grow into adults. All the jellyfish species described in this book follow a similar life cycle, though their polyp stages usually go unnoticed. Some other species lack a polyp stage altogether. [Note that the comb jelly on page 61 belongs to a different phylum from all the other species in this chapter]

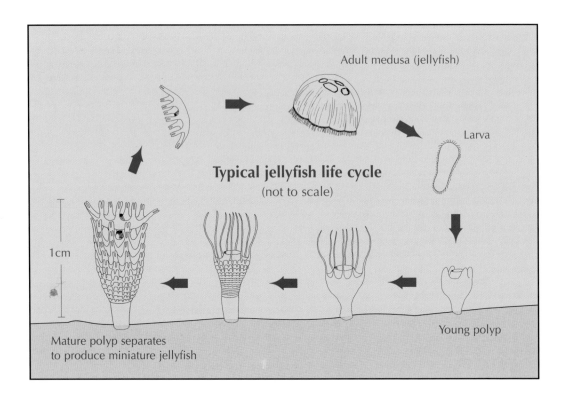

Adult medusa (jellyfish)

Larva

**Typical jellyfish life cycle**
(not to scale)

1cm

Young polyp

Mature polyp separates
to produce miniature jellyfish

# Beadlet anemone - *Actinia equina*

This individual has very prominent acrorhagi (blue bulges)

## Beadlet anemone - *Actinia equina*

The beadlet anemone is usually seen on rocky shores or in very shallow water. Underwater, its dense mass of tapering tentacles can be fully appreciated but when exposed to air between the tide-marks it retracts to avoid dehydration and then resembles a blob of jelly. The anemone's column is smooth but there may be small blue bulges, known as tubercles or acrorhagi, visible in a ring just below the tentacles. These structures, which contain large numbers of stinging cells, are very prominent in the anemone on the previous page and are important in aggression (see below). Beadlet anemones are most often coloured a deep red but can be green, brown or orange. There is increasing evidence, however, that many of these forms in colours other than red may be separate species. Unlike many sea anemones which produce planktonic larvae, the female beadlet broods its embryos for a few weeks before releasing them. Asexual reproduction also occurs, with internal budding seemingly producing miniature new anemones that develop inside both male and female adults. As well as having these varied reproductive arrangements, beadlet anemones also indulge in aggression against each other as they compete for favoured spots on the rocks. When two anemones come together, their tentacles touch but are then withdrawn from the area of contact. The acrorhagi (blue bulges) are the offensive weapons and, by bending towards their opponent, the aggressive anemones bring them into play. The bulges swell up before firing off a barrage of stinging harpoons and their surface may then peel off and remain attached to the target where it continues to cause damage. Such a bout ends when one of the combatants retreats. [Up to 5 cm across]

## Strawberry anemone - *Actinia fragacea*

The column of this dark red anemone bears characteristic bright green spots, so the derivation of its name is obvious. The strawberry anemone has a very similar shape and form to the beadlet anemone but is larger than its close relative and is found in slightly deeper water. For a long time classified as simply a different colour form of the beadlet, it is now recognised as a separate species. Unlike the beadlet, it does not appear to brood its young. [Up to 10 cm across]

## Gem (or wartlet) anemone - *Aulactinia verrucosa*

Despite the similarity of its name, this small and pretty anemone is a totally different species from the jewel anemone (pages 46-47). Often found in lower shore rock pools, it is mainly restricted to western and south western British coasts. The usual colouration is a blend of pink and grey with green markings around the mouth. The relatively few (48 or so) tentacles are translucent with attractive opaque spots. A few of the "warts" or "gems" that give rise to the anemone's common names are visible around the edge of its disc in the photograph. These warts, which are arranged in rows (some white and others dark) on the column are much more obvious when the anemone is closed. When tightly contracted, they make the anemone look like a small sea urchin skeleton without the spines. Young gem anemones are brooded within the parent. [Up to 5 cm across]

## Snakelocks anemone - *Anemonia viridis*

The snakelocks anemone prefers the brightly lit, seaweed-rich areas of rocky reefs in shallow water (top photograph this page) to the darker world of cliffs and overhangs which many anemone species inhabit. It can also be found in pools on the shore and on kelp fronds or, in the case of small individuals, on eel-grass strands. The two hundred or so long wavy tentacles are very sticky and are often a rich green colour with beautiful purple tips; they are unusual in that they cannot be fully retracted. The tentacles may obscure the short and squat column which is tapered and irregular in cross-section. The sun-seeking habit of the snakelocks is related to the fact that the tissues of its tentacles contain large populations of special symbiotic algae. In this close association, the algae gain protection and a supply of carbon dioxide and nutrient salts; the host anemone benefits from organic compounds synthesised by the algae using sunlight as the energy source. The algae may also help to remove waste products

Snakelocks among seaweed on top of a reef

from its host's tissues. Snakelocks in deep or murky water are often a dull grey colour and this may be due to their algal populations becoming depleted in low light conditions. This species of anemone also has some sort of relationship with Leach's spider crab, *Inachus phalangium* (see page 88). The crabs seem content to reside around the base of smaller anemones but, when a larger anemone is their home (bottom photograph), they can be found living right in the

Small spider crab residing in snakelocks

centre. The snakelocks is absent from most of the east coast of Britain. [With its long tentacles, can be up to 20 cm across]

Snakelocks anemone - *Anemonia viridis*

# Dahlia anemone - *Urticina felina*

The dahlia anemone has a sturdy appearance, with its short squat column covered in warts and its rather stout tentacles, but it is nevertheless a beautiful animal. A powerful predator, it can catch and devour active prey such as prawns and surprisingly large fish. Dahlias can occur in a variety of different colours (see photographs) and often have attractive banding on their tentacles as well as radiating patterns on the large oral disc. Gravel or shell fragments are usually stuck to the column so that, when the anemone is fully retracted, it is surprisingly inconspicuous. Dahlias are often seen singly but can also occur in dense patches at the bottom of shallow rocky gullies. Such aggregations are a marvellous sight to the passing diver, but must spell doom to many an unwary

small fish. The surge conditions found in such gullies will of course make it more difficult for the anemones' prey to avoid the grasp of their tentacles. [Up to 20 cm across]

Dahlia anemone - *Urticina felina*

Dahlia anemones in the Menai Straits

# Plumose anemone - *Metridium senile*

There are few finer sights, in our waters or anywhere else, than a group of plumose anemones swaying in the current. Very familiar to divers, they are prominent animals and occur in large numbers covering expanses of seabed or wreckage at many of the best diving locations. In its fully active state, the plumose anemone has a tall smooth column topped with a crown of very numerous fine, slender tentacles which give the characteristic feathery appearance. When withdrawn, it appears as a contracted little mound (see front right of photograph above). Individuals may be white, orange, green or brown in colour. Tentacles are usually, but not always, the same colour as the column (see above). Plumose anemones show a definite preference for areas of strong water flow, hence their frequent positioning on rock pinnacles or prominent pieces of wreckage. On wreckage, they seem to favour vertical surfaces such as on upright spars, rails and plates to horizontal positions. They may also be abundant in muddy areas, as long as there is some firm anchorage available. While normally most obvious down below the seaweed zone, plumose can be seen in shallow shady spots such as under overhangs and on jetty pilings. With fine delicate tentacles, these anemones are unsuited to capturing the large animals, such as fish, that form the food of several other species. Instead, they specialise in smaller prey and their enzyme secretions can break down the shells of small planktonic crustaceans. As well as passing prey to the mouth in the usual anemone-like fashion of flexing whole tentacles, the plumose can use the hair-like flagellae and mucus strings on each tentacle to transfer food down to the oral disc. [Up to 30 cm tall]

Plumose anemone - *Metridium senile*

## Trumpet anemone - *Aiptasia mutabilis*

The trumpet anemone is essentially a Mediterranean species that, in Britain, is limited to the far south west. Here, it can be quite common, large numbers are found in Torbay for instance, but its kelp-like colouring means that it may stand out less than other anemones. The overall brown or khaki is broken up by distinctive white or pale blue lines on its disc which radiate out from the mouth. [Can apparently reach up to 15 cm across but usually 5 cm or less]

## *Actinothoe sphyrodeta*

A very common small anemone on southern and western coasts, it can be found individually or in groups on rock faces. Most individuals are white all over but the disc is sometimes orange. The column and tentacles are always white. There are usually faint dark vertical stripes on the column, particularly visible when the anemone is contracted. This species can be confused with the all-white

or white-orange forms of *Sagartia elegans* (see opposite) but *Actinothoe* has untidier-looking tentacles which are fewer in number, and no suckers on its column. It is sometimes found attached to the large sea squirt, *Phallusia mammillata*, see page 173. [Up to 2 cm across]

36

## *Sagartia elegans*

Individuals of the form with patterned disc and tentacles

This anemone can be found in several different colour forms which, at first glance, look like separate species. The main photograph shows a group of these anemones of the form with patterned disc and tentacles; it was taken beneath the famous arch of Cathedral Rock at St Abbs (south east Scotland). The smaller photograph, taken in Cornwall, shows individuals of the following forms: white tentacles-white disc, white tentacles-orange disc and pink tentacles-variable coloured disc. A further permutation, with orange tentacles and a variable coloured disc, is quite rare and makes five colour forms in all. Regardless of tentacle and disc colour, the anemone's column is usually dull orange and is covered with small wart-like suckers that are most obvious when the tentacles are withdrawn. Sticky white threads are sometimes released by the anemone if disturbed. Reproduction can either be sexual

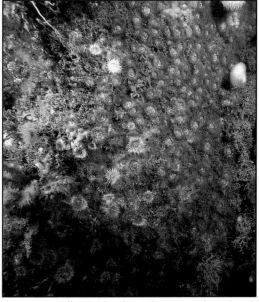

Different colour forms of *Sagartia* on the same rock

or by an asexual process where fragments of tissue separate from the base and form new anemones. [Up to 5 cm across]

## Sagartiogeton undatus

An elegant anemone that can be quite common in sandy areas. Its base is usually attached to a stone or shell buried beneath the surface of the sand, but the anemone's column is often tall enough to stand well clear of the seabed when it is fully extended. The column, an overall yellowish brown, has faint stripes running up it and there may be dark spots near the top. The disc has an attractive pattern, usually in grey and cream, while the long slender tentacles are translucent. There are two thin dark lines running down each tentacle, a useful distinguishing feature. The whole anemone can contract down into a very small mound when disturbed. [Up to 12 cm tall]

## Sagartiogeton laceratus

This species can perhaps best be described as a small, brightly coloured version of *Sagartiogeton undatus* (above). It can be found attached to shells, worm tubes or stones, sometimes partly buried in sand. The column is usually pale orange and there is also plenty of orange on the attractively patterned disc. Pale V-shaped stripes stand out from darker markings around the bases of the slender tentacles. The tentacles have no dark lines running down them (as do those of *S. undatus*). As indicated by the second part of its Latin name, *S. laceratus* undergoes asexual reproduction where parts of its base break away (by laceration) and form new anemones. This is why the edge of the anemone's base tends to be very irregular in shape and several individuals are often found living together. [Up to 6 cm tall]

## Daisy anemone - *Cereus pedunculatus*

Can form carpets of many individuals or be found singly, often living on muddy seabeds where their bases are anchored to stones buried in the sediment. The anemone's long, slender column is hidden in the mud so its large disc and numerous short tentacles lie virtually flush with the mud's surface. Daisy anemones also live on rock where their columns are hidden in crevices. The disc may be a uniform brown or be

attractively patterned in various colours, while the tentacles can be striped or mottled. There is often a bold splash of colour around the mouth.

Young anemones develop within the parent and are released as fully formed miniatures. [Up to 10 cm across, more usually about 5 cm]

## *Peachia cylindrica*

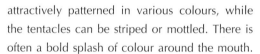

This species has a distinctive appearance with 12 tentacles (much fewer than most anemones) that are mottled in brown, grey and white with repeating W-shaped markings down their length. Its disc can be patterned with similar colours or be all white. The anemone lives in sandy habitats and the tentacles are usually seen lying out flat across the seabed while its long slender column is buried in the sand. This column has a

rounded end (rather than the adhesive base of most anemones) and acts as an effective anchor which stops the anemone being washed away by

currents and swell. [Tentacle span up to 15 cm across but usually much smaller, buried column up to 30 cm long]

## Parasitic anemone  -  *Calliactis parasitica*

Common in the south west but rare further north, this species of anemone is usually found on second-hand mollusc shells inhabited by the large hermit crab, *Pagurus bernhardus* (pages 89-91). The column of the parasitic anemone is typically a dirty cream colour with brown spots or stripes, while the tentacles are a yellowish grey. The anemone's name is misleading because it is in no way a parasite. Both crab and anemone benefit from the relationship and both can live independently; the anemone sometimes being found on stones or empty mollusc shells (top photograph, opposite page). Such a loose liaison is not true symbiosis either, and is normally referred to as commensalism. When living together, the crab will benefit from extra protection provided by the anemone's stinging tentacles against predators such as fish and cuttlefish. In return, the anemone receives extra scraps as the crab messily rips up its food, and

gets free transport to different feeding locations. As the crab moves around, the anemone will often bend over so its tentacles "sweep" the seabed. Parasitic anemones can recognise hermit crab shells, probably by smell, and will actively transfer onto one if they are living on another substrate. First of all, they reach out and attach their oral disc to the shell with the aid of discharge capsules. They then detach their base from its current anchorage, and swing it across onto the hermit's shell. The crab plays no active part, but co-operates by keeping still. Occasionally, more than one parasitic anemone will be found on a single hermit crab. The bottom photograph on the opposite page shows a crab carrying three anemones, it could barely move under the weight. This anemone can occasionally be found living on the claw of a spiny spider crab (page 85). [Anemone up to 8 cm tall]

## Parasitic anemone - *Calliactis parasitica*

Living alone

Three anemones on a single crab

41

# Cloak anemone - *Adamsia carciniopados*

The anemone's white tentacles are visible between the hermit crab's legs

This species, common around most of Britain, also lives on hermit crabs, but the association is much more intimate than that between the parasitic anemone and its host. The cloak anemone's host is the small hermit crab, *Pagurus prideaux* (page 92). The anemone is never found living without a crab, and tends to stay with the same crab for life. Its base, which is usually brown or white with garish magenta spots, is wrapped right around the crab's mollusc shell home, hence the name "cloak". The anemone's white tentacles are positioned down between the legs of the crab in an ideal position to pick up the scraps which inevitably result from the crab's feeding activities. By secreting a hard extension to the crab's residence, the anemone removes the crab's usual need to seek larger shells as it grows. This reduces stress for the crab and of course also prevents the anemone itself from being abandoned. When touched, the anemone releases sticky white threads from its "cloak" as a defence mechanism. This will often be seen to occur if a host hermit bumps into a rock or worm tube as it retreats hurriedly across the sea bed (top photograph, opposite page). On some anemones, the bright pink spots are obscured and it is only the emergence of these threads that give away their presence. The bottom photograph on the opposite page shows that a cloak anemone does not make its host invincible. A harbour crab (pages 80-81) is tucking into the remains of a small hermit crab while its cloak anemone appears to have been carefully peeled off and discarded. The anemone has discharged some threads in a last act of defiance. ["Cloak" up to 7 cm across]

## Cloak anemone - *Adamsia carciniopados*

Defences activated

Not everyone is deterred. This harbour crab has removed and discarded the anemone, before tucking into the hermit crab.

## Sea loch anemone - *Protanthea simplex*

As its name suggests, this sea anemone is known mainly from Scottish sea lochs where it can be extremely abundant, particularly on vertical rock faces. Colour is pale orange through to white, with the column usually a denser shade than the long and slender translucent tentacles which cannot be retracted. Food particles that bump into any part of the anemone's body get trapped by its sticky surface and can then be consumed. This is presumably an adaptation to its sea loch environment where suspended food may be less abundant than on open coasts. [Up to 7 cm across, usually smaller]

## Fireworks anemone - *Pachycerianthus multiplicatus*

The most striking feature of this spectacular species is its huge size. It is a burrowing anemone (like *Cerianthus lloydii*, opposite) and lives on muddy seabeds within its own tube. The long outer tentacles, all white or white with brown bands, may coil up if disturbed but cannot be retracted into the column. The shorter and stiffer inner tentacles are usually pale brown. It is quite a rare sight, mainly restricted to fairly deep water (10 to 130 m) in Scottish sea lochs. [Tentacle crown up to 30 cm across, column up to 30 cm tall, tube up to 1 m long!]

# Burrowing anemone - *Cerianthus lloydii*

This very common species of burrowing anemone (like the unusual fireworks anemone, opposite below) is not classified as a true sea anemone. Rather than attaching itself to a rock or similar firm surface, it lives in a soft felt-like tube that is constructed by specially adapted discharge capsules. Although the tube can reach up to 40 cm in length, only its uppermost rim will protrude

Dislodged anemone and its tube

above the sand or mud in which the remainder lies buried. The anemone's tentacles are usually all that is visible. The innermost set are short and stiff, while the outer ones are longer and sometimes attractively banded. The tentacles themselves are not retractable but, when disturbed, the whole anemone shoots back into its tube. The smaller photograph, of a dead anemone in its dislodged tube, shows the relative proportions of anemone and tube. [Tentacle crown up to 10 cm across, body/column up to 15 cm long]

# Jewel anemone - *Corynactis viridis*

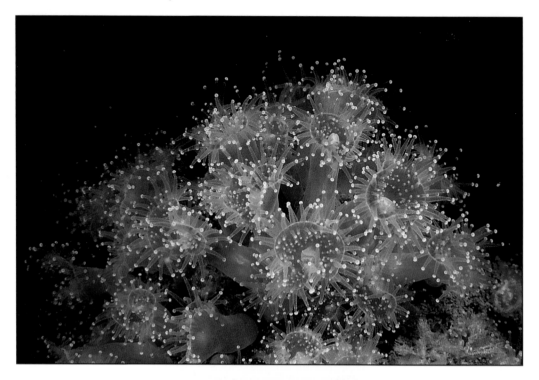

Small individually but impressive collectively, jewel anemones produce some of the most beautiful underwater scenery around Britain. The anemones occur in an amazing variety of colours: pinks, purples, reds, oranges, yellows, greens, browns and more can all be seen on a single rock face. Their capacity for prolific budding (asexual reproduction) means that the different colours are not totally mixed but occur in distinct patches. When this

Jewel anemone patchwork

anemones are most impressive in locations off the south west of England, Wales and western coasts of Scotland, and are largely absent from the east coast of Britain. An individual jewel anemone is an attractive animal in its own right too. It has one hundred or so translucent tentacles, with distinctive white or brightly coloured rounded knobs on the tips; these knobs are laden with large numbers of discharge capsules of different types. The mouth

effect is combined with very clear water, the result is astounding, though they can also be found on the shore and even in quite muddy locations as long as there is good water movement. Jewel is located on a minute cone in the centre of the tentacles. Jewel anemones are actually more closely related to corals than to the other anemones. [Up to 2.5 cm across]

Jewel anemone - *Corynactis viridis*

## *Parazoanthus anguicomus*

This species belongs to a group of anemone-like creatures (sometimes called colonial or encrusting anemones) that are not true sea anemones. Clusters of its attractive white polyps arise from a shared encrusting base and a careful peek amongst the stems of a colony reveals that they are joined. The tentacles are in two rings with one set tending to reach straight up while the other set is more splayed. This species is generally found in quite deep water and this photograph was taken on a Cornish wreck in 35 metres where the colony covered large areas of superstructure. However, I have quite often seen it in shallower water off the west coast of Scotland. *Parazoanthus axinellae*, a very similar species, is coloured bright yellow and has a sparser crown of tentacles. [*P. anguicomus* up to 3 cm tall, *P. axinellae* slightly smaller]

# Devonshire cup-coral  -  *Caryophyllia smithii*

Abundant around much of Britain and not only Devon, this species is the only common stony coral in our waters. Stony corals are similar to sea anemones but produce hard chalky skeletons to support and protect their bodies. They are usually colonial animals, and their fused skeletons can then form large coral structures. Cup-corals, however, live alone and do not fuse together, although many can live within close proximity. Their hard skeleton consists almost entirely of calcium carbonate and is cup or goblet-shaped, with pronounced ridges radiating out from the centre and running over the rim. As the creature lays down more skeletal material at its base, it is pushed upward and stays in the top of the cup. With tentacles fully extended, cup corals resemble small anemones. There are many different colour forms and some have a very attractive zigzag pattern of dense colour around the central mouth, while others are all white. The tentacles end in small but obvious knobs. The underlying skeleton may be largely obscured (as above) or quite obvious (as in the cup corals in the foreground of the photograph of a cotton-spinner on page 163). Empty cup skeletons can sometimes be seen after the polyp has died. [Up to 4 cm across]

# Dead men's fingers - *Alcyonium digitatum*

Like some species of anemone, the soft coral colonies known as dead men's fingers can cover large expanses of rocky cliffs or seabed and so create their own brand of underwater scenery. Many of the rock faces around St Abbs in south east Scotland (see photograph opposite) are excellent examples. Dead men's fingers are generally orange or white. In northern Britain, both of these colour forms are very common but in the south the white form dominates. Each "finger" is a colony of tiny animals that has formed a mutual skeleton of gelatinous material (hence *soft* coral) strengthened by embedded calcareous spicules. Until a colony reaches a height of about 5 cm it remains unbranched but, once larger than this, it tends to divide into several lobes. If arranged in a single plane as they

often are, a group of lobes then appears like a hand. When active and feeding, the animals that make up the colonies extend their translucent tentacles and the lobes have a characteristically attractive "furry" appearance. In the photograph (above) the animals in the lobe at the lower right corner have retracted their tentacles. In the autumn, most colonies stop feeding and withdraw their tentacles for several months, while they prepare to spawn. Entire rock faces can then be covered by what look like knobs of expanded polystyrene. When feeding is resumed, an outer skin is shed, along with any encrusting growths that settled while the tentacles were out of action. As with so many animals that rely on suspended food, they are more abundant in areas of moving water. [Up to 20 cm tall]

Dead men's fingers - *Alcyonium digitatum*

White and orange dead men's fingers

# Red fingers - *Alcyonium glomeratum*

Close-up of tentacles

Not to be confused with the orange form of dead men's fingers, red fingers are a separate but closely related species of soft coral. The feeding tentacles are white, as opposed to the translucence of those belonging to dead men's fingers, and make a striking contrast against their red background. This allows extreme close-ups (main photograph) to show their full beauty. Further differences between the two species are that

Colonies showing tentacles extended and withdrawn

red finger colonies can be taller, and often appear slimmer, than those of their close relative and that they have a distinctly knobbly appearance when the tentacles are withdrawn (see bottom lobes in smaller photograph). Red fingers are far less common than dead men's fingers and are only found on the western side of Britain. [Up to 30 cm tall]

# Pink sea fan - *Eunicella verrucosa*

Rocky slopes dotted with pink sea fans are the sort of wonderfully exotic sight that is usually associated with warmer seas. Around Britain, this species is restricted to south west England and south Wales. It is most common at depths greater than 10 metres, although the odd individual is found in shallow water. Like dead men's fingers, sea fans are colonies of tiny creatures. The sea fan is classified as a gorgonian or horny coral. A skeleton composed of a dark brown protein (gorgonin), reinforced with calcium carbonate, runs through the fan and is covered with fleshy tissue from which the tentacles of the numerous polyps emerge to feed. This tissue gives the fan its colour; pink, pale orange or occasionally white. Fans only branch in one plane which is usually at right angles to the prevailing current, thus giving each animal the maximum opportunity for feeding. The fans grow slowly, at around 1 cm per year, and the largest may be over 100 years old. While fairly flexible, they can easily be dislodged from the rock by careless fin or arm movements and will die once knocked flat, so please take care! The pink sea fan is one of the very few marine animals protected by the Wildlife and Countryside Act, and it has also been identified as a priority Biodiversity Action Plan species. Sea fans are often used by dogfish as an anchoring point for their "mermaid's purse" egg cases. In some locations, a tiny species of sea slug lives on the fans and feed on their polyps, although these are thought to re-grow so the fan survives. The slugs' colouration and shape match those of the polyps so they are very difficult to spot. [Fans up to 50 cm tall in most areas but up to nearly 1 m tall in the Channel Islands]

# Northern sea fan - *Swiftia pallida*

Always white or pale grey, the northern sea fan looks like a pale and rather straggly version of the pink sea fan. It is widely distributed around Europe as a whole but, on British coasts, it is only common on the west coast of Scotland where it is found in sheltered and fairly deep water. By contrast, the pink sea fan is only common in the south west of Britain so you are unlikely to see the two species together. There is a small area of overlap in south west Ireland. The northern sea fan does not have the same legal protection as its pink relative but is just as vulnerable to physical damage and pollution. [Northern sea fans up to 20 cm tall]

# Slender sea pen - *Virgularia mirabilis*

The sea pens are feather-shaped colonies of anemone-like animals and are related to the soft corals and sea fans. Unlike those animals, sea pens are adapted for life on a muddy or sandy seabed. The lower part of the stem acts as an anchor buried in the sediment while the remainder bears the polyps,

usually on side-branches. The slender sea pen has short side-branches which produce the slim feathery appearance. It can withdraw completely into the mud when disturbed. Several of these sea pens are often found living quite close together, as in the photograph. [Up to 50 cm tall]

## Phosphorescent sea pen - *Pennatula phosphorea*

The thick stem and large side leaves of this species gives it a much more bulky appearance than that of the slender and tall sea pens. Its bright white polyps contrast attractively with the deep red "body". As its name suggests, it can produce brilliant flashes and pulses of light if touched at night. Common in Scottish sea lochs and sheltered inlets, it can be found around most of Britain but is apparently absent from the south coast. [Up to 30 cm tall]

## Tall sea pen - *Funiculina quadrangularis*

This superb creature is quite an unusual finding but is included here because it is so spectacular. Reaching up to over 2 metres tall, its stem has a slight curve as it leans gently in any current. Its huge size should distinguish it from the slender sea pen, and it also has a much less fluffy appearance. The square cross section of its stem (that gives rise to the second part of its Latin name) is a further distinctive feature. In the background of the photograph, a few slender sea pens can be seen, dwarfed by their neighbour. The tall sea pen has been recorded from as far away as Japan and New Zealand but, around Britain, it is restricted to very sheltered water on the west coast of Scotland. [Up to over 2 metres tall]

## Oaten pipe hydroid - *Tubularia indivisa*

A species often found in large aggregations on rock faces exposed to strong currents. Numerous long and very thin straw-like stems rise up from a mat of tangled fibres to form dense bunches. These stems support polyps that have pink bodies bearing a crown of long white, rather droopy, tentacles. The reproductive parts appear like a bunch of grapes near the centre of the crown. This species lives for about a year and produces a creeping larva rather than a free-swimming medusa. A number of types of sea slug prey on this hydroid and can often be found amongst the stems, or crawling up them to feed on the polyps (page 125). The slugs are not deterred by the hydroid's stinging cells, some even incorporating them for their own defensive use. [Up to 15 cm tall]

## *Hydractinia echinata*

Almost always found on the borrowed mollusc shells of hermit crabs, this hydroid species forms an obvious and distinctive pale pink or white "fur". A colony consists of an encrusting mat which supports different types of polyp. Some are tall with a tiny crown of anemone-like tentacles while others are short and tightly coiled. The various polyp types predominate on different parts of the shell and the presence of

the crab and its breathing currents are thought to affect their distribution and development. The larvae of this hydroid can detect a suitable hermit shell by its movement and attach themselves with stinging threads. They then form a colony by budding. [Tallest polyps reach up to 1.5 cm]

## *Obelia geniculata*

The obvious hairy "fuzz" often found on fronds of kelp and other brown seaweed is produced by colonies of this hydroid species. The "fuzz" is a forest of tiny stems with numerous small side branches that each bear a tiny polyp. The stems have a very characteristic zigzag form which distinguishes this

species from other similar hydroids. A dusting of silt can sometimes collect on the colonies and this unfortunately obscures their wonderful structure. Unlike the hydroids on the previous page, this species belongs to the type (thecate) whose polyps have tiny protective cups into which they can withdraw. Distribution is worldwide. [Stems up to 5 cm tall]

## Sea beard  -  *Nemertesia antennina*

This hydroid is found growing in distinct clumps. The main stems, pale orange or buff in colour, are unbranched but have numerous feathery side branches. Each stem in the clump is a colony of individual polyps, whose tentacles add to the furry appearance. The clumps provide shelter and food for small animals of all kinds and the white beads of sea slug eggs can often be seen

entwined round individual stems. When looking at this species, it is very easy to see why hydroids are also known as sea-firs. The brightly coloured creatures, visible on the rock face around the sea beard clumps, are jewel anemones (pages 46-47). [Up to 25 cm tall]

# Compass jellyfish - *Chrysaora hysoscella*

This species is easily identified by the attractive radial pattern of dark brown V-shaped markings on its "umbrella" or "bell". An additional dark circle in the centre of the pattern completes the appearance of an old-fashioned compass rose. Twenty-four slender (marginal) tentacles hang down from the edge of the umbrella while there are four much more noticeable (oral) arms in the centre. The marginal tentacles extend when the animal is hungry and, on capturing prey which may be any sort of planktonic animal, they contract in order to pass the food to the oral arms. When feeding is finished, the marginal tentacles remain contracted. Eight sense organs, each one situated between groups of three marginal tentacles around the umbrella's fringe, enable the jellyfish to maintain its orientation in the water. Young fish belonging to the cod family, particularly whiting, can often be found swimming around and between the compass jellyfish's tentacles (see bottom

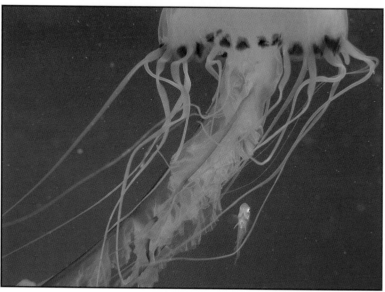

photograph). This provides the youngsters with protection from predators such as larger fish, who will avoid the tentacles, but it seems to be uncertain as to how the young fish themselves avoid being stung and eaten by the jellyfish. The sting of this species can sometimes cause a painful reaction on exposed human skin. [Umbrella up to 30 cm across]

# Lion's mane - *Cyanea capillata*

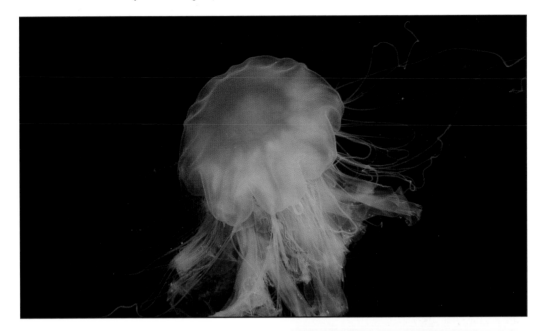

The lion's mane jellyfish is an impressive animal but it can leave a painful impression if approached too closely! Its tentacles, covered with powerful stinging cells, stretch up to three metres long when extended and it is quite easy to swim into them before the main body of the jellyfish is spotted. Fragments of tentacles, left on buoy ropes for example, also retain their stinging power. The lion's mane umbrella usually has brown markings and is rather flat with its edge formed into large lobes. There are four large arms surrounding the mouth, but these are far shorter than the tentacles. The tentacles are arranged in eight bunches, with each bunch containing over a hundred tentacles, the oldest of which is often coloured dark red. As with the compass jellyfish (opposite), small fish are often seen sheltering amongst the tentacles (see bottom photograph). The lion's mane is quite common off north, east and west coasts of Britain but is rare in the Channel. Its close relative, the smaller *Cyanea lamarckii*, is found all round Britain and tends to be more common than the lion's mane in the south. Its umbrella is usually a shade of blue or purple, although sometimes

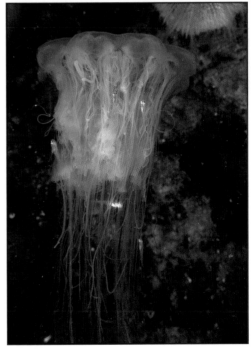

yellow, and there are fewer tentacles in each of its bunches. The sting is less powerful than that of the lion's mane. [*Cyanea capillata* (lion's mane) up to 50 cm across, *Cyanea lamarckii* up to 30 cm across but usually much smaller]

## Moon (or common) jellyfish - *Aurelia aurita*

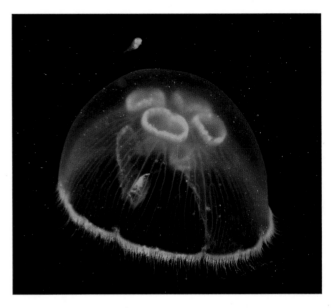

Without long trailing tentacles, the moon jelly's most distinctive features are its reproductive organs. These appear as four relatively opaque horse shoe-shaped tissues, visible in its almost transparent umbrella. The umbrella itself is saucer-shaped and has numerous small tentacles around the edge, like a fringe. It has eight marginal sense organs like the compass jellyfish, (page 58) and these are marked by slight indentations in the rim. The four arms near the central mouth are used in feeding, though planktonic food can also be captured in mucus anywhere on the umbrella and be transported to the mouth by a system of grooves lined with tiny beating hair-like cilia. The short peripheral tentacles can also capture prey with their stinging cells, though these are not of sufficient power to bother humans. [Up to 25 cm across]

## Barrel jellyfish - *Rhizostoma octopus*

This species is the largest jellyfish found in British waters. Not often found close to the shore, it is usually seen from boats or by divers decompressing on a shot-line, for whom its massive pulsating form makes an interesting diversion. There are no markings on the whitish umbrella except for its dark rim, and no peripheral tentacles. The eight central arms are fused for much of their length to form a dense bunched mass. This structure bears hundreds of tiny mouth openings, each surrounded by miniature tentacles bearing stinging cells. Creatures striking the tentacles and small enough to pass through a mouth opening will be ingested. The sting is harmless to humans and there are even reports of these jellyfish being eaten by eighteenth century fishermen. *Rhizostoma* is apparently very sensitive to the vibration from ships and will move downwards as one approaches. [Up to 80 cm across]

## *Bolinopsis infundibulum* (example of a comb jelly)

Strictly speaking, a comb jelly should not be in this chapter at all. Comb jellies belong to the phylum Ctenophora, and not to the phylum Cnidaria which contains all the sea anemones, corals, hydroids and true jellyfish. Nevertheless, comb jellies resemble small jellyfish and their group is thought to be an evolutionary offshoot of the cnidarians. The characteristic feature of comb jellies is the set of (usually 8) comb rows that run down the outside of the gelatinous body. These rows are a series of small plates formed from the fusion of tiny hair-like cilia. The plates beat rhythmically to drive the animal mouth-first through open water; with some comb rows beating faster than others if a turn is required. The shimmering combs are often beautifully iridescent in sunlight and those of some species give off luminescence at night if disturbed. Many comb jellies have tentacles that, while lacking the stinging cells of cnidarians, have adhesive cells for catching their prey which can include small fish. *Bolinopsis infundibulum* has an almost transparent oval body and can be abundant near the surface during the spring and summer. Other species of comb jelly are also common, including the small round sea gooseberry. Note that the name "sea gooseberry" is also sometimes used as an alternative to "comb jelly" in describing the whole group. [*Bolinopsis* up to 15 cm long, sea gooseberry up to 3 cm long]

# Chapter 4
# WORMS

Few groups of animals would initially seem to be of less interest than the worms, but some of those that live in the sea are surprisingly attractive and definitely worthy of further scrutiny. The term "worm" is rather misleading because it tends to be applied to any creature that is long and wriggly. Different groups of animals, that vary enormously in terms of their biology and level of sophistication, fall into this category as a result. For ease of reference, different types of worm are all included in this chapter. Representatives of the flatworms and ribbon worms are dealt with on page 64-65, and the rest of the chapter belongs to the segmented worms. The characteristics of the different groups are described below.

## Flatworms

Flatworms, forming the phylum Platyhelminthes, are primitive leaf-shaped animals. They are regarded as being more advanced than cnidarians (sea anemones, jellyfish) because of the way that they are organised. The cells that make up cnidarians are grouped to form tissues, but that is as far as organisation goes. The tissues of flatworms work together to form organs, that perform particular functions such as digestion. Flatworms are the lowliest animals to have this level of organisation, and may possibly represent the ancestral group from which all the other more advanced animals are descended. Flatworms are still classified as simple because they lack a body cavity, and this means that their internal layout has to remain fairly crude. Also, they only have a single opening to the digestive system, which has to serve as both mouth and anus. Flatworms like the candy stripe (page 64) are free-living, but many species are well known parasites of land animals; tapeworms and liver flukes are examples.

## Ribbon worms

Ribbon worms make up the phylum Nemertea and, as their name implies, are thin and long. They are quite primitive but are slightly more advanced than flatworms. They have an anus as well as a mouth, which means that the intestine can utilise a more efficient one-way system where undigested and digested food are separated. This is a big advantage over the flatworms, whose food and excretion products have to enter and leave the body by the same route. Ribbon worms also have a circulatory system and possess more advanced muscles and nerve networks. A trunk-like extending structure, the proboscis, is used both in trapping prey and in defence. Two ribbon worms species are described on page 65.

Worm egg capsules attached to seaweed

## Segmented worms

In contrast to flatworms and ribbon worms, segmented worms (pages 66-73), belonging to the phylum Annelida, are quite complex animals on a par with most crustaceans and molluscs. They have a proper body cavity, which permits the development of sophisticated internal organs, while the nervous system is of sufficient complexity to support a variety of behaviour patterns. Virtually all the segmented worms found in the sea, and all those species described in this chapter, belong to the bristle worm sub-group. Typically, they have heads which bear intricate jaws, antennae and sense organs, while the remainder of the body consists of a series of less specialised segments which are fairly similar to one another. Many of these worms move freely from place to place but, because they burrow into soft sea beds or stay hidden amongst the organic debris on rocky sea beds, they are rarely seen by snorkellers or divers. Some species, however, leave a very obvious clue to their existence every year in the early spring. They attach their green egg capsules to seaweed (see above), and these can be seen in huge numbers, forming an obvious part of the scenery. In general, however, the segmented worms that make themselves most obvious to the diver are those that have given up the free-living way of life, and live in a tube that they have constructed. The strawberry worm (page 67) and all the worms after it in the chapter are tube worms. Many of these species have heads and sense organs less well developed than those of their active relatives, but they have a crown of very specialised feathery tentacles. These can be surprisingly beautiful, and are extended into the water column where they are used both for respiration and for collecting suspended food.

# Candy stripe flatworm - *Prostheceraeus vittatus*

Found on mud or amongst stones and seaweed, the candy stripe flatworm is so thin and flexible it gives the impression of almost flowing across the seabed. Colouration is distinctive, cream with very marked dark "pin-stripes", and its body is often thrown into folds at the edges. There are two tentacles at the head end of the body which make the worm look rather like a sea slug, but these are a totally different group of animals (see Chapter 6). Mobile flatworms such as *Prostheceraeus* are carnivorous and feed on slow-moving, sedentary or dead animals. Their smooth gliding motion is produced by thousands of tiny hair-like cilia on the underside of the body acting in unison. [Up to 3 cm long]

# Bootlace worm - *Lineus longissimus*

Individuals of this very slender ribbon worm species can grow to over 30 metres in length, so it could be thought of as Britain's largest animal! More usually, they are around 5 metres long when extended, but the entire body is rarely visible and will contract rapidly if touched.

Colouration is typically dark brown to almost black, sometimes with a slight iridescent sheen. The head is only slightly wider than the rest of the body and has several eyes on each side, though these are difficult to discern against the dark pigment. [Up to 30 m long]

# Football jersey worm - *Tubulanus annulatus*

Although they may not instantly remind you of a football jersey, the markings on this ribbon worm are extremely distinctive. Three slender white stripes run along the reddish brown body, one on the back and one down each side. These are complemented by 50 or so well-spaced white rings that encircle its body. Apart from its markings, this species is quite similar in

form to the more commonly encountered bootlace worm. The football jersey worm is sometimes found crawling across a sandy or stony seabed but is often hidden under stones or in crevices. It has a very wide distribution in the northern hemisphere and is found on the west coast of North America, all across the Atlantic and in the Mediterranean. [Up to 1 m long]

## Sea mouse - *Aphrodita aculeata*

A strange-looking animal that does not even look like a worm. The upper side of its broad and flattened body is covered with a felt-like fur while, round its edges, are some stout dark bristles and a fringe of silky iridescent hairs that can appear to glow gold, yellow and blue. The telltale worm-like segments are only visible on the body's underside. The sea mouse lives on bottoms of muddy sand and is usually buried with only its hind end exposed; it is thought to prey on other worms as well as eating carrion. The array of body hairs prevents mud particles being drawn in with the animal's breathing current. [Up to 20 cm long]

## Paddleworm - (Family Phyllodocidae)

Most of the other segmented worms described in this chapter live permanently in burrows or tubes. Paddleworms often hide under stones but they can also be seen roaming freely over the seabed. They are mainly active carnivores and can be watched inspecting hollows in the sand and making a grab for tiny shrimp-like crustaceans. These worms may produce large amounts of mucus when disturbed. The name paddleworm arises from the overlapping leaf-shaped paddles that fringe both sides of the body and can be used to help the worm swim. It is difficult to distinguish between the many species of paddleworms within the family Phyllodocidae. Definite identification requires very close examination. The gelatinous green egg capsules shown in the photograph on page 63 were laid by paddleworms. [Up to 60 cm long]

## Lugworm - *Arenicola marina*

Whether on the beach or underwater, the cast of the lugworm is a very familiar sight. The worm itself is hardly ever seen, as it has no need to leave its U-shaped burrow. Lugworms feed on the organic material in muddy sand and have to swallow enormous amounts of sediment in order

Worm cast

to obtain adequate nutrition. The coiled casts represent processed material ejected by the worm while the small hollow in the sand nearby is where water, for respiration, and fresh sediment is drawn down. The long burrow is lined with mucus to prevent its collapse. [Worm up to 25 cm long; coiled casts up to 20 cm across]

## Strawberry worm - *Eupolymnia nebulosa*

This photograph shows the worm's body, coloured in orange-pink with white spots, that gives rise to the name. It is, however, unusual to see anything more than the strawberry worm's long sticky tentacles (also shown in the photograph) which spread out over the sea bed to collect food particles.

The tentacles shrink back rapidly if touched, but are not fully retractable. The body of the worm, and the slimy tube in which it lives, are usually hidden beneath stones and shell fragments on muddy sediment. Where many worms live close together, a real tangle of tentacles may cover the seabed. [Body up to 15 cm long, tentacles 20 cm long or more]

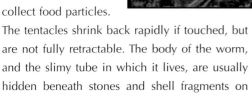

## Sand-mason - *Lanice conchilega*

The sand-mason worm builds a gritty tube from grains of sand glued together with mucus. The top of the tube stands proud of the sea bed, and is crowned with a tuft of finger-like extensions, so the overall effect is that of a miniature tree. Large numbers usually live together, resembling a sparse forest as in the photograph. The worm itself is hardly ever seen, but it extends its sticky tentacles along the "tree's" branches to catch suspended food, and also out over the sea bed to pick up deposited food particles and any sand grains required for tube maintenance. The branches, which are orientated across the current, also serve to slow down water flowing past, so more suspended material collects around them. [Body up to 30 cm long, tube to 45 cm but only top 5 cm shows]

Forest of sand-mason tubes

## *Myxicola infundibulum*

This worm's distinctive tentacles are webbed along almost all their length, so the crown resembles a small cone or funnel. It is just the flat, pointed and darkly coloured tips of the tentacles that are clearly separate. *Myxicola* lives in sandy and muddy areas and only the very end of its thick gelatinous tube, if any at all, protrudes from the sediment. The outer edges of the crown will be virtually flat on the seabed when fully expanded. This species is very shy and may rapidly withdraw into its tube when approached. The photograph shows a group of three individuals, but they are usually seen singly. [Tentacle crown up to 5 cm across]

# Fan worm - *Bispira volutacornis*

This species of fan worm is most abundant in the south, where its attractive feathery tentacles are commonly seen emerging from the nooks, crannies and overhangs along the sides of rocky gullies and reefs. The worm lives in a tube, constructed from mucus and mud, that looks like a roll of thick grey paper. Tubes may be up to 20 cm long, but most of their length is usually hidden within the rock crevice. When extended, the all-white or brown-and-white banded tentacles form a double spiral. The tentacles have a number of functions, including the collection of suspended food and the extraction of oxygen from the seawater. They are also scattered with sense organs such as eyes. A shadow passing overhead, or sudden movement anywhere in the vicinity, will cause them to be rapidly withdrawn into the tube. The worms tend to live in small groups and while the retraction of individuals may often appear synchronised, those in some groups show marked variations in sensitivity and response time. A tube with tentacles withdrawn, and showing the typical pinched appearance, is at the top right of the photograph. [Tentacle crown up to 5 cm across]

## Peacock worm - *Sabella pavonina*

The peacock worm can be a very striking animal, possessing a wonderful feathery fan of tentacles that emerges from a prominent but slim tube. These tubes are found attached to stones in sand and mud, and also on rocks or shipwrecks. The tentacles are usually colourful, often with red banding, and as with all tube worms they disappear quickly back into the tube if not approached with care. Water-borne particles captured by the worm's tentacles are sorted so that the largest are discarded, the smallest are eaten and intermediates are mixed with mucus and used for tube construction. The photograph shows a group of peacock worms living on the steep side of Loch Duich in West Scotland. Many peacock worms, such as those found living amongst eel-grass in sandy estuaries, are less obvious because their tubes are partially buried in the seabed. [Tubes up to 25 cm long, tentacle crown up to 15 cm across]

# Coral worm - *Salmacina dysteri*

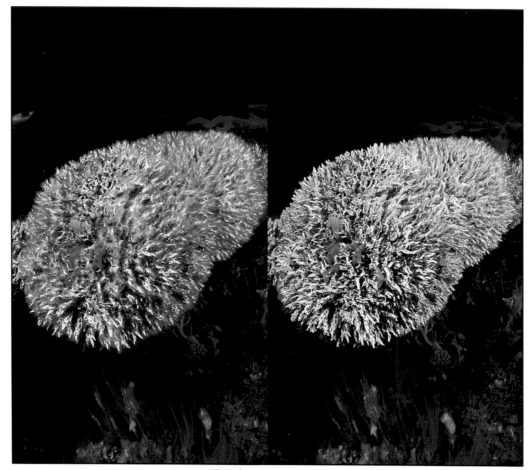

Tentacles out                    Tentacles withdrawn

The coral worm is like *Serpula vermicularis* and *Spirorbis spirorbis* (pages 72-73) and different from the other tube worms described in this chapter, in that its tube is hard and completely rigid. Its name arises because the chalky tubes of many individuals are joined together to form a coral-like mass. Colonies can be found attached to any hard surface; the photographs show one that has encrusted an undersea cable. The fine tentacles of each worm give the colony a "furry" appearance when extended for feeding (left-hand photograph), but this changes dramatically when they are withdrawn (right-hand photograph). The coral worm differs from *Serpula*, *Spirorbis* and several other similar worms in that none of its tentacles are modified to form a special plug for the tube. The thin chalky tubes are manufactured almost entirely from calcium carbonate, the worms extracting calcium from seawater. Tube material is secreted by special glands, and is then moulded into shape by the collar near the worm's front end. Coral worms engage in some asexual reproduction (budding) and a new individual can be formed at the rear end of an existing one. The new worm will crawl part-way down the parent's tube and dissolve a small hole so that its own tentacles can emerge. If the parent tube is badly damaged by this activity it may become separated from the rest of the colony. [Individual worms tiny but colonies are often 15 cm across]

## *Serpula vermicularis*

Close-up of *Serpula* tubes showing tentacles and trumpet-shaped plugs

### Serpula vermicularis

*Serpula* is an impressive but very wary worm and its beautiful spread of red, pink or white tentacles tends to shoot back into its home tube at the slightest disturbance. With patience, however, the tentacles are eventually seen to re-emerge and can be examined along with the trumpet-shaped structure that forms a plug to the tube when the tentacles withdraw. The rigid chalky tube is anchored at its base but much of its length may stand proud of the seabed. Several tubes are often entwined around each other and, in sheltered water locations such as some Scottish sea lochs, large masses of worm tubes can be found (see smaller photograph). These masses provide shelter and attachment points for a huge number of other creatures such as brittle stars, crabs, scallops, sea squirts and clingfish to name a few. [Worms up to 7 cm long, masses of tubes can be nearly 1 m tall]

### *Spirorbis spirorbis*

This worm lives permanently in a small coiled tube which is cemented on to the fronds of green or brown seaweed. Its favourite home is the saw wrack seaweed (*Fucus serratus*) that has distinctive serrated edges to its fronds. Many of the white chalky tubes are often found together. The worm has a crown of feeding tentacles that can be seen extended from the tubes of several of the worms in the photograph. One of the tentacles is specially modified to form a plug for the tube when the crown is withdrawn. A number of worm species build similar tubes; including other *Spirorbis* species that favour different habitats such as red seaweed or stones. [Tube coil is just a few mm across]

# Chapter 5

# CRUSTACEANS
## Crabs, lobsters, prawns, shrimps & barnacles

Crustaceans can be thought of as the aquatic animals which wear suits of armour. This armour is jointed, and crustaceans belong to the larger grouping, Arthropoda, which means "jointed leg". Insects are also arthropods and, in many ways, the crustaceans are aquatic insects. All the familiar animals such as lobsters, crawfish, crabs, prawns and shrimps belong to the same sub-group of the crustaceans, the Decapoda, and have a similar body plan. They have ten legs (hence the name), the first pair of which are often claws. The head and thorax are fused and covered by a single section of armour, known as the carapace. The abdomen, or tail, is protected by further sections of armour and may be obvious as in the lobsters, prawns and shrimps or much reduced and tucked up as a flap underneath the rest of the body, as in the crabs. Barnacles, an unexpected inclusion in the crustacean category, are in a separate sub-group from these more familiar members. They are described in more detail on page 102.

## A suit of armour, the benefits and drawbacks

The suit of armour worn by crustaceans has obvious benefits, providing good protection against predators, rigid anchorage points for powerful muscles and hard surfaces for crushing, cutting and grinding their prey. The major drawback is that it has to be shed periodically to allow growth. As a crustacean grows to fill its shell, it forms a soft leathery coat beneath the outer casing. At moulting time, the shell splits at a pre-determined point and the animal, clad in its soft coat, eases itself out. The top photograph, opposite, shows a prawn found struggling to free itself from its old armour. All the limbs, tiny mouth parts and even the eyes have to be removed from their casing. The middle photograph, opposite, shows the discarded armour suit of a swimming crab; the opening at the back where the owner climbed out is visible. Such a suit is so complete that it can easily be mistaken for a dead crab. Having left the old suit, a soft crustacean swells itself up with water to create some growing room and the process of hardening up new armour then begins, taking several days in the case of large crabs and lobsters. The soft animal is obviously very vulnerable and has to stay as well hidden as possible. Once hard, it will have a particularly large appetite and seek food vigorously before eventually becoming relatively inactive and listless as it prepares for the next moult. Reproduction is affected by moulting, because the female of many species is only receptive after she has just shed her shell, so the moulting cycles of crustaceans can really be seen to dominate their lives. The bottom photograph on this page shows the sequence of armour suits worn and discarded by a shore crab kept in an aquarium for three years. The amount of growth between successive moults is substantial.

## Regenerating limbs

Although moulting inserts dangerous interludes into the life of a crustacean, it also provides the opportunity for regenerating limbs. A leg or claw that is damaged or seized by a predator can be jettisoned by the animal, which breaks it off deliberately at a particular point near to its base. A new limb can then start to form inside the shell and will emerge at the next moult. This is why crustaceans will often be seen with a very small leg or claw, though this will catch up with the other limbs over subsequent moults. The process can lead to a "right-handed" crab or lobster becoming "left-handed". If the large crushing claw is lost, the return to a fully equipped state can be hastened by converting the smaller cutting claw to a crusher and then growing a new cutting claw.

Moulting prawn struggling free from its armour

The suit of armour discarded by a moulting crab

Series of discarded suits showing the growth of a crab

## Breeding

All the crustaceans described in this chapter have a larval phase that drifts as plankton in the open sea. On first hatching from the eggs, these larvae look very different from their parents. They develop through various larval stages, feeding, growing and moulting at each one. Gradually taking on more adult features, they eventually settle down on the seabed as immature miniature versions of the adult. After many more moult cycles, they are ready to breed. The drawing below shows a typical crab life cycle (the number of larval stages and adult moult cycles varies from species to species). There are photographs of velvet swimming crabs in pre-mating embrace, mating and carrying eggs on page 79. There are also photographs of shore crabs (opposite), harbour crabs (pages 80-81) and hermit crabs (page 91) with their partners before mating.

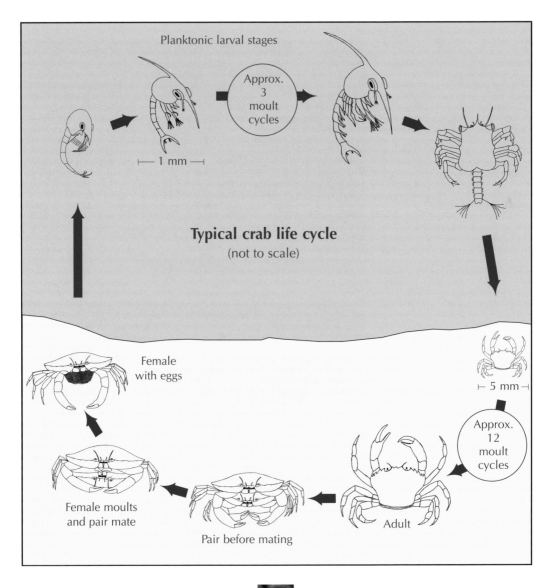

Planktonic larval stages

Approx. 3 moult cycles

⊢ 1 mm ⊣

**Typical crab life cycle**
(not to scale)

Female with eggs

⊢ 5 mm ⊣

Approx. 12 moult cycles

Female moults and pair mate

Pair before mating

Adult

# Shore crab - *Carcinus maenas*

Pre-mating pair

The shore crab is a familiar animal to anyone who has ever looked under stones on a beach or dangled a bacon-baited string into a muddy creek. Very common on the shore and in shallow water, it is seen less often by divers than many crabs because it is most abundant in muddy estuaries and inlets. The pre-mating pair in the main photograph show how colour can vary amongst shore crabs. The larger male has the typical green and yellow colouration

Small shore crab eating a colleague's claw

swimming crab group, the paddles on this crab's rearmost legs are less well developed than those of the velvet swimming crab and harbour crab (pages 78-81) and it is a much poorer swimmer. Shore crabs are extremely hardy and, by tolerating a wide range of conditions in terms of salinity and exposure to air, can live in virtually fresh water or barely any water at all. They eat a variety of animal prey such as worms, shrimps and any

while the female underneath has the deeper orange worn by some crabs that are thought to not have moulted for a considerable time. The male is holding onto the female until she moults and then they can mate. The shore crab's carapace shape can be seen clearly in the photograph of discarded moults on page 75. Though it belongs to the

molluscs that they can break open. Cannibalism also occurs; the crab in the smaller photograph probably tore the claw he was eating from a colleague who was soft after moulting. Some populations of shore crabs suffer a high level of infestation from the parasitic barnacle, *Sacculina carcini* (page 103). [Carapace up to 8 cm across]

# Velvet swimming crab - *Necora puber*

The body of this abundant and widespread crab is covered with short greyish-brown hairs that provide the velvet-like appearance. The most **notable features** however, are the bright red eyes and the blue lines on its legs and claws. As in all swimming crabs, the final section of the rear-most pair of legs is flattened to form a **swimming paddle**. Velvet swimming crabs tend to be

Crab breaking into top-shell

pugnacious and, when encountered, may rear up and spread their claws in defiance rather than shrinking away into a crevice. Very common on rocky and stony sea beds, they can also be found on sandy and muddy bottoms where they may dig themselves in. They are **versatile feeders** and, being fast-moving and agile, can catch prey such as fish and prawns. All sorts of bottom-living animals like worms and molluscs are also taken. The smaller photograph on this page shows a velvet swimmer tackling a top-shell. Lacking the strength to simply crush such a shell, the crab gradually chips away at its opening with one claw while the other claw is used for holding and

## Velvet swimming crab - *Necora puber*

Pair before mating

turning. Although often actively carnivorous, some populations of velvet swimmers have been found to eat large quantities of seaweed. Pairs of crabs in **pre-mating embrace** (top photograph, this page) are a common sight. As in most crab species, the female can only mate when soft just after shedding her armour, so a male will find a female and hang on to her until she is ready to moult. He carries her tucked beneath his body and continues to move around and behave much as normal, possibly helping her out of the old armour when the time arrives. The middle photograph shows a pair of velvet swimmers actually mating. This is easily distinguished from the pre-mating embrace because the female is upside down and therefore lying underside-to-underside with the male. The bottom photograph shows the ultimate result of such a union, a female is carrying a large mass of **fertilised eggs** (noticeably granular and usually orange) between her abdomen and underside. An egg-carrying female is said to be "in berry". [Carapace up to 10 cm across]

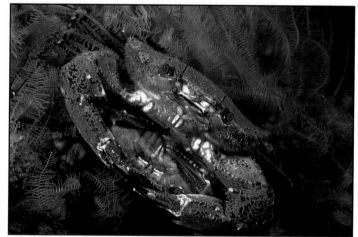
Pair in the midst of mating

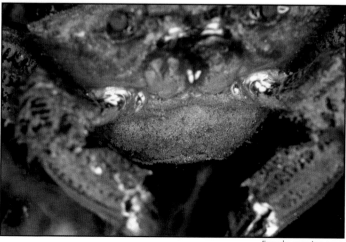
Female carrying eggs

# Harbour crab - *Liocarcinus depurator*

Pre-mating pair in defensive posture

This species, often simply known as the swimming crab, is similar in shape to the velvet swimming crab but is more lightly built and pale pink or reddish brown in colour. These swimming crabs are almost always found on sandy seabeds, sometimes buried with only antennae and pale brown eyes showing. If disturbed they have various options; making a rapid escape, assuming an aggressive posture with claws spread wide or simply moving a short distance and submerging into the sediment. They are very capable swimmers with a distinctive style. The rear-most pair of legs are used for paddles, as by all swimming crabs, but those of this species seem particularly well suited to the purpose, judged by both appearance and performance. The body is propelled rapidly sideways, just above the sea bed, with the other legs held stiffly out from the body for maximum streamlining. When swimming, the paddles are a blur of motion but, when stationary, the characteristic mauve spots on the blades can be seen (see smaller photograph on this page). Like

Rear view, showing the distinctive mauve spots on the paddles

the velvet swimmer, pairs of these crabs are often seen in pre-mating embrace. The main photograph on this page shows such a pair in the typical claws-spread defensive posture; the much smaller female is joining in even though she has only one claw! The photograph opposite shows a pre-mating pair that were being followed by another male. All three crabs appeared very watchful and the "spare" male seemed as though he was waiting for an opportunity to "steal" the female. [Carapace up to 7 cm across]

# Harbour crab - *Liocarcinus depurator*

Pre-mating pair of crabs, being followed by another male

# Edible crab - *Cancer pagurus*

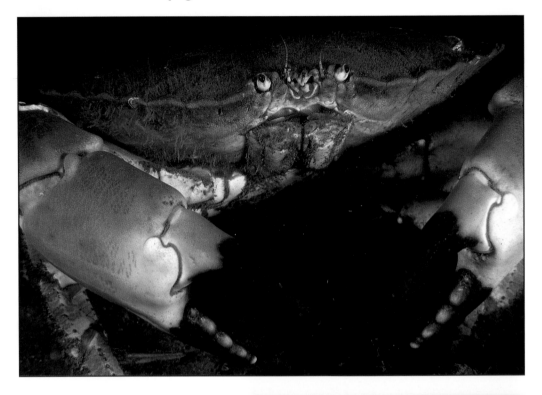

The edible crab has a thick, oval shell with a very distinctive "pie-crust" edging. The claws are large but the legs appear relatively small. The overall colour is a pink-brown while the claws have noticeable black tips. Compared to the swimming crabs, edible crabs are built very much for strength rather than speed. This is reflected in their prey, and molluscs that might require hours of patient manipulation from a velvet swimming crab can be quickly crushed by an edible crab's powerful claws.

Digging pit in search of food

Conversely, they would find chasing small fish much more of a challenge than their nimbler relatives. Edible crabs are found in a variety of habitats at all depths. On rocky bottoms, they will live in crevices while, on soft seabeds, they dig themselves into the sediment. Here, they may also dig huge pits in their hunt for burrowing prey such as clams and worms, and a muddy seabed can become a mass of craters, each containing a busily excavating edible crab (see smaller photograph). As in all crabs, the abdomen of the female is broad and rounded while that of the male is narrower. [Carapace up to 25 cm across, but rarely more than 15 cm]

# Masked crab - *Corystes cassivelaunus*

This crab is common on sandy seabeds, though it may be overlooked because it is usually only the tips of the antennae and claws that protrude from where it has dug into the sand. Masked crabs will often only be spotted when inadvertently disturbed and they may just move a short distance before digging in again. On occasion, they attempt to dig directly into the hiding place of another masked crab and the smaller photograph shows the altercation that resulted after one such intrusion. The crabs' short legs give them a relatively slow, lumbering gait. Males (as shown) have very long claws, up to double the length of the body, but those of the female are much shorter. Unlike that of the other crabs listed here, the carapace of the masked crab is longer than it is broad. Once tilted upright, the body is therefore the perfect shape to slip rapidly beneath the sand while the crab digs with its legs.

Territorial dispute

While buried, the antennae are held together to form a snorkel-like tube through which the crab can draw clean water. To the imaginative, the ridges on the carapace look like a human face, hence the name. [Carapace up to 5 cm long]

## Square crab (or mud runner) - *Goneplax rhomboides*

The square crab has a most distinctive appearance and is unmistakable whether viewed from the front or the back. Its carapace is much broader than it is long and has very pointed corners, while the long eye-stalks and very long slender claws enhance the exotic image. Both photographs show male crabs. The female, which is seen less frequently, has much smaller claws.

This species is quite an unusual sighting but it is abundant in some areas with muddy sand. While many of the crab species described in this chapter can dig themselves into soft sediments, the square crab is different in that it makes a permanent burrow. This burrow is normally a shallow 'U' shape with two exits, but there may also be side tunnels. Crabs are often seen sitting at the entrance to their burrows, but they can also be found hiding in crevices beneath boulders or out and about on patches of mud between the boulders. Their detached claws are regularly seen lying on the seabed in areas where they live, presumably lost in fights or during struggles with predators. [Carapace up to 5 cm across]

# Spiny spider crab - *Maja squinado*

The carapace of this large crab is quite circular, shaped like a dome and covered in many short spines, with longer and more pointed spines around its edges. There are two large points between the eyes, looking almost like horns. It has long and slender legs, and the claws are not much bigger than the walking legs, except in large males. Spiny spider crabs can be found on most seabed types, often resting in the open or wandering free rather than hiding in crevices. Despite these habits and their large size, some individuals can be very difficult to spot because of the camouflaging seaweed or sponge placed on their carapace and legs, which blends in perfectly with their surroundings (see smaller photograph). Spiny spider crabs can sometimes be seen grouped together in large heaps, or moving across the seabed in substantial numbers, presumably on their way to or from such a function. The heaps are found in the summer, and may stay in the same place for a few months, often containing up to a hundred individuals. Huge

Spiny spider crab with sponge camouflage

mounds of up to a thousand crabs have even been reported. Crabs moult in the centre of the heaps and, while soft, are protected from predators by all the crabs outside them. The heaps also mean that newly moulted (and therefore receptive) females will have suitors readily available, so heaping seems to play an important part in the breeding of these crabs. Spiny spider crabs have a varied diet, feeding on seaweed and encrusting animals such as hydroids. They can also often be found eating carrion. [Carapace up to 20 cm across]

# Sea toad (or great spider crab) - *Hyas araneus*

Sea toad eating a jellyfish

## Sea toad (or great spider crab) - *Hyas araneus*

This spider crab is intermediate in form between the large bulky spiny spider crab (page 85) and the very spindly small spider crabs (below and page 88). The "great" in one version of its common name is therefore rather misleading. Its carapace is roughly triangular, being much wider at the rear than at the front. It is usually reddish brown on the back with a dirty white underside, but can be disguised by seaweed, sponge or other encrusting growth. These crabs are often seen clinging to kelp stems (see photograph on this page)

where they graze the small attached seaweeds as part of their omnivorous diet. Kelp stems may also give them a good vantage point for catching passing jellyfish which they appear to relish (see photograph opposite). Sea toads are regularly found munching on the moon jellyfish, *Aurelia aurita*, (page 60) but it is not clear whether they can catch healthy jellyfish or whether they simply rely on coming across sickly individuals. The sea toad appears to be much more common off northern coasts than in the south. [Carapace up to 8 cm across]

## Long-legged spider crab - *Macropodia rostrata*

A small spider crab with an extremely "spindly" appearance. In addition to having a smaller body (especially in comparison to leg length) than crabs such as the sea toad (above) and Leach's spider crab (page 88), it lacks protrusions to the carapace behind the eyes, so the eye stalks are more prominent. It is very common but the emaciated features, coupled with the crab's habit of attaching camouflaging seaweed or sponge to its carapace and legs, can easily

result in it being overlooked. It is most likely to be spotted while wandering across a sandy or muddy seabed, away from any seaweed cover. A very similar species, the slender spider crab *Macropodia tenuirostris*, has a longer promontory at the very front of its carapace, though this is usually obscured by the seaweed camouflage. [Carapace up to 1.5 cm across]

## Leach's spider crab - *Inachus phalangium*

This small spider crab has a triangular carapace. The legs are very long and slender but the claws, which are usually held folded under the body, are fairly sturdy, particularly in the male. Carapace, claws and even legs are often covered with sponge and pieces of algae, which may make the crab virtually invisible. These crabs are very often seen hiding around the base of a snakelocks anemone or, if it is a large anemone, sitting within its tentacles (main photograph this page and

Territorial dispute

page 30). In some areas, virtually every snakelocks has its own resident crab. The two crabs in the smaller photograph on this page appeared to be in dispute over the favoured space beneath the anemone's tentacles. The nature of the relationship between crab and anemone seems to be something of a mystery. *Inachus phalangium* is very difficult to distinguish from *Inachus dorsettensis*, the scorpion spider crab, particularly as the distinguishing features on the carapace are usually obscured by camouflaging sponge. For the sharp-eyed, *I. dorsettensis* has a broad U-shaped tip to the promontory of its carapace between the eyes, while that of *I. phalangium* comes to a narrower point. [Carapace up to 3 cm across]

# Common hermit crab - *Pagurus bernhardus*

The common hermit crab can be very abundant on both rocky and sandy seabeds, and small individuals are often found in pools on the shore. Colour is typically pale orange-brown with darker reddish markings. The claws are covered with numerous bumps and lines of quite prominent spines. Only the front part of a hermit crab is protected by the usual crustacean armour which has to be shed to allow growth. The top photograph on page 90 shows a hermit crab with its recently shed armour in front of it. The soft rear end is protected by a disused mollusc shell which is carried around by the crab. When threatened, the whole body can be withdrawn into the shell with the larger right-hand claw forming a barrier across the entrance. As the crab grows, a larger shell is sought out and the hermit will only change home after a prolonged and thorough inspection of the new shell. The bottom photograph on page 90 shows a crab that seemed to be engaged in such an inspection, an ambitious gesture since the original mollusc owner was still in residence. Young hermits live in shells from smaller molluscs like winkles, while adults inhabit the larger whelk shells. The rear end of the hermit is coiled so that it fits neatly into the shell and is equipped with small hooks for clinging to it, while the last two pairs of walking legs are used as struts to support the shell's weight. The top photo on page 91 shows the rear end of a hermit which is visible because a badly damaged shell is being occupied. It was found in a small inlet with a very large number of hermit crabs, where the great demand for shells had presumably led to such a sub-standard item being used rather than discarded. Hermit crabs are versatile feeders and can prey on other animals, scavenge on bottom deposits or filter food from the surrounding water. Male hermits can be seen dragging females around for a few hours prior to mating (bottom photo, page 91) though the crabs found doing this are often surprisingly small. The parasitic anemone can sometimes be found living on mollusc shells carried by the common hermit crab (see pages 40-41). Other animals, such as worms, may live on the shell or even inside it with the crab in order to gain protection and/or extra food. [Carapace up to 4 cm long but mollusc shell home makes crab look much larger]

## Common hermit crab  -  *Pagurus bernhardus*

Recently-moulted hermit crab with discarded armour

Examining a potential home

## Common hermit crab - *Pagurus bernhardus*

Hermit crab living in badly damaged shell, the usually hidden abdomen is visible

Pair before mating

## *Pagurus prideaux*

This small hermit crab tends to be a darker reddish-brown than *Pagurus bernhardus*, the common hermit crab. The shape of its claws and carapace are often quoted as distinguishing features but I find the large dark eyes are the most obvious difference. What is more noticeable than the features of the crab itself, however, is that almost all individuals carry a cloak anemone (described in more detail on pages 42-43). The cloak anemone on the crab in the photograph is very obvious but this is not always so. With its white tentacles positioned down underneath the crab, the anemone can be very hard to spot, particularly if the distinctive magenta spots are obscured by a fine dusting of silt. The anemone stays with the hermit for life and frees it from the need of changing to larger second-hand mollusc shells as it grows (the armour on the front part of crab still needs to be moulted of course). In return for providing the crab with additional security and growing space, the anemone gets extra food and these crabs have even been observed placing food into their cloak anemone's mouth. *Pagurus prideaux* is usually found on seabeds of muddy sand below low tide level; small hermits seen in rock pools and on clean sand will very often be young *Pagurus bernhardus*. [Carapace up to 1.5 cm long but mollusc shell home makes crab look much larger]

# Spiny squat lobster - *Galathea strigosa*

Squat lobsters look like a cross between crabs and lobsters. Their long body is flattened, with the tail tucked up underneath it (see smaller photograph). The tail can be used as a paddle for rapid backward escape. This widespread species is particularly striking, with a brilliant red carapace decorated by blue patches and stripes, and long red-tipped claws covered with a "fur" of brown spines. It is rarely

Side-on view showing tail tucked up

seen in its full glory, however, because it usually hides away in narrow crevices, often clinging upside down to the rock ceiling and shrinking further out of view when approached. It is most likely to be seen out and about at night. [Body, including tail, up to 10 cm long]

## *Galathea squamifera*

This small squat lobster is very common on the shore and in shallow water, but it normally stays hidden from view and is only seen if stones are turned over. It will then escape quickly, moving backwards with rapid flicks from its tail. The individuals in the photograph were found hiding amongst *Serpula* worm tubes (see pages 72-73). Colour is usually a greenish brown but youngsters are more reddish. This species is thought to be mainly a filter feeder, eating suspended organic material. [Body, including tail, up to 6 cm long]

# Long-clawed squat lobster - *Munida rugosa*

Long slender claws and bulbous eyes peering out from a crevice or hollow are the hallmarks of this abundant animal. The long-clawed squat lobster is an extremely common sight in areas where the seabed is a mixture of stony crevices and mud, such as around the inlets and sea lochs of Scotland's west coast. On muddy slopes with a scattering of boulders, an individual can be found in virtually every sheltering place. The overall colour is red or reddish brown but the claws, about double the length of the body, are the most distinctive feature. Its antennae are nearly as long as its claws. This species appears much less timid than the other squat lobsters and is content to remain partially out of its shelter if approached carefully, often spreading its claws in defiance. It may even edge forward to investigate the intrusion and is thus easy to photograph. Long-clawed squat lobsters can sometimes be seen carrying dead crabs or other carrion and a dispute between two neighbours over such bounty or the occupation of a hiding place may also be witnessed. [Body, including tail, up to 8 cm long but claws can make it look larger]

# Common lobster - *Homarus gammarus*

A "left-handed" lobster at home

A "right-handed" lobster out and about

## Common lobster - *Homarus gammarus*

A magnificent but all too rare sighting, the lobster's appearance is unmistakable: dark blue armour with pale yellow markings and long bright red antennae. The powerful claws are quite different in shape; one (usually the right-hand one) is heavier and is used for crushing, while the other is a sharper cutting tool. Lobsters are normally found hiding within rocky holes or inside wrecks during the day but, when watched for a while, may move cautiously forward to investigate the intruder. They will usually only emerge from their lair at night, but can occasionally be seen roaming the seabed during the day (see bottom photograph, opposite page). Such encounters normally happen in deep water but lobsters may also be found in very shallow water if there is sufficient shelter. They feed on a variety of bottom-living animals, alive or dead, and are also well known cannibals; it is difficult to keep more than one lobster in an aquarium because the first one to moult will usually be rapidly consumed by its companion. They generally move by walking, but can also swim rapidly backwards in short bursts by using the powerful tail as a paddle. Mating is thought to occur in the late summer, but females can store the sperm packet over the winter so the eggs are not fertilised and laid until the following summer. They may then take a further year to hatch into the free-swimming larvae. After a few moults, these transform into miniature lobsters and settle on the sea bed. Large lobsters moult only very occasionally, if at all, and can become covered with barnacles and other encrusting organisms. They may live for up to 50 years. [Body up to 75 cm long but rarely more than 30 cm]

## Crawfish (or spiny lobster) - *Palinurus elephas*

The crawfish is a large animal with strong, spiky body armour but no claws. Colouration is orange brown with yellow markings. The antennae are longer than the body and heavily built, with large spines at their bases so that they can be used as defensive weapons. Crawfish live in rocky areas and may often be found in holes, but they are also more likely to be seen wandering free over  the seabed during the day than the common lobster. They are rare in water shallower than 20 metres however. Numbers of these animals have been greatly reduced by intensive fishing, chiefly carried out by divers. Unlike the common lobster, the crawfish is only found on western coasts of Britain. [Body up to 50 cm long but rarely more than 35 cm]

## Scampi (Norway lobster, Dublin Bay prawn) - *Nephrops norvegicus*

The host of common names used to describe this species is probably a reflection of its considerable commercial importance across much of Europe. It is also called langoustine or simply "nephrops". The body colour is pale orange and the large eyes are jet black. It is a relative of the common lobster and, though smaller and much more slimly built, is similar in form. The slender claws are about as long as the rest of the body and carry rows of distinctive spikes. Scampi live in deep water (usually greater than 40 metres) and in burrows on muddy bottoms. They are therefore rarely seen by divers. The burrows can form complex systems of horizontal tunnels and scampi will spend most of their time there. They come out to hunt, mostly at night, for food such as small crustaceans and worms. The animal in the photograph was found in the shallows close to St Abbs harbour and had almost certainly just fallen off a returning fishing boat. [Body up to 20 cm long]

## Common prawn - *Palaemon serratus*

Prawns and conger eel sharing a crevice

These animals are a very common sight in the nooks and crannies of wrecks and rocky reefs, and are often found in groups. The almost transparent body has numerous delicate brown lines and there may also be obvious yellow bands and blue markings on the legs. The front two pairs of legs bear nippers, which are used to pick up small pieces of food as the prawn walks across the seabed. Prawns can also swim, either backwards in rapid bursts using the tail fan, or forwards using the small flaps beneath the abdomen for propulsion.

Surprisingly, groups of prawns often seem to occupy the same crevice as predators such as velvet swimming crabs, lobsters and congers (see main photograph). [Up to 10 cm long]

# Pink (or northern) prawn - *Pandalus montagui*

This attractive crustacean lives up to both these versions of its common name. Though the body is translucent, it has characteristic pink patches on its carapace and bright red lines marking its body. Channel coasts represent the southern extent of its distribution and it seems to be most commonly seen while diving in the north of Britain. Unlike the common prawn (page 99), it is rarely found in pools on the shore. It is thought that some pink prawns are female throughout their life while others start as males and become females later. They live for about 3 or 4 years, having bred from their first year. This species is also known as the Aesop prawn. [Up to 16 cm long, but usually about 5 cm]

# Brown shrimp - *Crangon crangon*

Dug in, only the eyes are left showing

The brown or common shrimp is abundant in sandy areas but can be very difficult to spot because of its mottled sandy colouration and tendency to remain buried with only the eyes exposed. The shrimp in the main photograph was more obvious than usual because it was walking across dark sand that had been turned over by an excavating crab. The head and body of the brown shrimp are more flattened than those of a prawn and they lie almost flush with the sea bed, rather than being lifted up by the legs. The front pair of legs bear claws that are more substantial than those carried by many small prawns. It has a varied diet which includes animals such as small worms and crustaceans plus algae and detritus. If a brown shrimp is seen walking across the sand it may rapidly dig itself in (as shown in the sequence of smaller photographs), using an odd shuffling motion to get started, followed by sweeping movements of its long antennae to brush sand over its back. [Up to 9 cm long]

## Barnacle - *Balanus perforatus*

Barnacles belong to a totally different sub-group of crustaceans from all the other animals described in this chapter. On first glance, one would not even think of them as crustaceans at all. With their sedentary life-style and limpet-like shape, barnacles look rather like molluscs, which was how they were classified until 1830. As with other examples in the animal kingdom, it was an examination of their larvae (which look like those of other crustaceans) that revealed their true identity. A barnacle has been described as being "like a shrimp which glues its head to a rock, lives in a house and kicks food into its mouth". This is entirely accurate, as glands on the young barnacle's head produce a special cement for permanent attachment, the usual crustacean armour is modified to form flat plates that make up the "house", and the limbs form a sieve for catching plankton. When observed underwater the rhythmic sweeping of the feeding "sieve", looking rather like a grasping hand, can be seen (see photograph). The limb is rapidly withdrawn if sudden movement is detected and small fish can sometimes be seen trying to nip it off before this happens. Barnacles occur in large populations on the shore and in shallow water. They are hermaphrodites (simultaneously male and female) and mating usually occurs between neighbours. The resulting embryos develop in the body of the parent until they become free-swimming planktonic larvae, and these then develop further until they are ready to take on adult life. It is at this point that they glue themselves head-first to a rock and quickly assume the familiar adult form. There are several very similar common species of barnacles, including other *Balanus* species, which have an identical basic lifestyle. *Balanus perforatus* has simply been included as an example of its kind. [Up to 3 cm across]

## *Sacculina carcini* (a parasitic barnacle)

Though classified as a barnacle, this bizarre animal has a strange parasitic form totally different from the normal hard-cased barnacles that live attached to rocks. Just as barnacles were identified as crustaceans from examination of their larvae, *Sacculina* is recognised as a barnacle by its larval form. A female *Sacculina* larva attaches to the surface of a young crab and then grows into branching roots which penetrate the tissues of the unfortunate host. The usual host species is the shore crab, *Carcinus maenas* (page 77), but other members of the swimming crab family are also affected. The parasite eventually produces a yellow or pale brown reproductive

Swimming crab with reproductive mass of *Sacculina* visible beneath

Parasitised shore crab with heavy encrusting growth

mass which is visible as a large lump beneath the crab's abdomen (see top photograph). The lump is distinguishable from the crab's own egg mass because it is smooth rather than granular. Eggs produced by ovaries in the lump are fertilised by male *Sacculina* larvae which have no adult stage. A crab affected by the parasite is prevented from moulting so it's carapace may become heavily encrusted with animals such as barnacles and tube worms (see bottom photograph). This is usually a more obvious sign of infestation than the lump of the parasite itself. In addition to interfering with moulting, *Sacculina* also feminises male crabs and they take on certain female characteristics such as a broader abdomen. *Sacculina carcini* is the best known parasitic barnacle but there are several other similar species which affect different groups of crabs, squat lobsters and prawns.

# Chapter 6
# MOLLUSCS
## Sea snails, sea slugs, bivalves, cuttlefish & octopus

The typical mollusc has a hard chalky external shell, formed in either one part (limpets, whelks) or two (mussels, scallops). Some molluscs however, have no shell at all (nudibranch sea slugs, octopus) or one that is hidden from view (cuttlefish) and these less typical molluscs are some of the most fascinating marine animals. Where present, the external shell is like a cover rather than the all-encompassing body armour of crustaceans. This means it can be gradually enlarged as the animal grows and does not have to be shed periodically, the same shell being kept for life. The phylum name, Mollusca, is derived from the Latin word for soft, in reference to the soft body typically enclosed in the hard shell.

## Main mollusc features

The soft body of a typical mollusc is composed of three main parts: a muscular foot, a visceral mass which contains digestive and reproductive organs and, thirdly, the mantle tissue that secretes the shell. The very strong muscular foot forms the base of the animal and represents most of its contact with the outside world. The head, where sensory organs such as eyes and tentacles are located, is formed from the front end of the foot. The mollusc shell is made up of a protein matrix reinforced by numerous calcium carbonate (chalk) crystals to produce a strong composite material like fibreglass.

## Unusual feeding machinery

An intricate feeding mechanism, the radula, is found in most molluscs (apart from the bivalves) but nowhere else in the animal kingdom. It is a ribbon of horny tissue, bearing teeth, which is drawn backwards and forwards across food like a file. It also acts like a conveyor belt in transporting the rasped off food to the digestive tract. The form of the radula varies between molluscs that browse vegetation and those that eat flesh. The hard working machinery is continually replaced, with new teeth produced at one end of the radula while worn teeth are broken off at the other end.

## Reproduction

Molluscs use a great variety of reproductive strategies. Some simply shed eggs and sperm into the water while others use internal fertilisation and attach their eggs to the seabed. Still others brood eggs within their bodies and produce youngsters which resemble miniature adults complete with shell. Closely-related species (some of the periwinkles for example) may use very different strategies from one another.

## Sea snails

These are the archetypal molluscs with a single hard shell, like limpets, whelks, top-shells and periwinkles. Many have a shell in the shape of a coil. They follow the basic mollusc body plan, as outlined above, quite closely.

## Sea slugs

Few animals arouse such interest relative to their size as the colourful sea slugs. Although some sea slugs have a reduced shell, most of the species encountered are of the nudibranch order which lack a shell entirely. The term nudibranch actually means "naked gill" because the gills have no shell or mantle cavity to protect them. Without a hard shell into which they can retreat, nudibranchs have to rely on other forms of defence. Special skin glands produce toxins to repel predators and some species have an even more impressive system whereby they feed on creatures with stinging cells (sea anemones, hydroids) and utilise the second-hand cells for their own defence (see page 125). All nudibranch sea slugs are hermaphrodites, having both male and female sex organs. When two come together to mate, there is usually double copulation with both individuals donating and receiving sperm. Sea slug egg masses are a very common sight attached to rocks, stones or hydroids. They are usually white and their appearance can vary from coiled flat ribbons to miniature strings of pearls. Only a fraction of the large number of nudibranch species that can be seen are described in this chapter. For a full listing, one of the more specialist texts needs to be consulted (page 225).

## Bivalves

These are molluscs with two halves to their shells such as mussels and scallops. Bivalves have no head and are the only molluscs to do without a radula. The name bivalve means "two shells" but the shell is actually a single structure. The narrow strip of shell joining the two halves has much less calcified reinforcement than the rest, so it can act as a flexible hinge. Though they appear static and rather unsophisticated, bivalve molluscs are highly specialised for their chosen way of life, namely filter feeding. The gills are enormous, far larger than would be needed just for respiration, because they are also used for collecting suspended food from the water. Numerous banks of cilia (tiny hairs) on the gills beat in unison to create a powerful water current through the body cavity while other cilia help to trap food particles and move them towards the gut. It is this filtering ability that can make bivalves dangerous

purveyors of food poisoning when harvested from polluted areas. In addition to relatively obvious bivalves, such as mussels and scallops, there are numerous other types that burrow deep into soft sediment. At the surface of the mud or sand, the only sign of their presence is the two openings of their water intake and outflow tubes (see photograph). These are rapidly withdrawn if any disturbance is detected.

Burrowing bivalve tubes visible at the sand's surface

## Cuttlefish and octopus

These fascinating animals, along with squid, belong to a specialised group of molluscs, the cephalopods. The muscular foot of typical molluscs has become the group of tentacles attached to the head (cephalopod means "head-foot") and the mantle tissue has formed a jet propulsion organ, but it is still difficult to visualise how the basic mollusc body plan has been adapted to produce such sophisticated animals. Rather than having separate nerve centres scattered round the body like other molluscs, these animals have them fused and enlarged to form a sophisticated brain which is enormous by the standards of invertebrates. [Invertebrates are animals without proper backbones - all the animals in this book, except for the fish, are invertebrates]. The cephalopod brain is responsible for sophisticated behaviour and these animals display the ability to learn and remember for several weeks.

# Limpets - (various *Patella* species)

Limpets belonging to the genus *Patella* are amongst the most familiar molluscs and are abundant on virtually all rocky shores. They have a robust conical shell that is usually seen jammed down tightly onto the rock surface where they live. If one is found while it is actively crawling along (see top photograph) the muscular foot and a pair of large head tentacles may be visible, along with numerous tiny tentacles around the very edge of the shell. Like so many animals that seem mundane at first glance, limpets have an interesting story to tell. They create a "home base" on the surface of a rock by grinding their shell (or the rock if it is soft) to make a perfect fit. This helps to prevent the animal drying up when the tide is out. When the tide is in, limpets leave

Limpet crawling

Rock showing a large limpet's home base, with other limpets nearby

their "home base" (visible as a scar on the rock, see bottom photograph) and go off to graze algae on the rock nearby. They have to return home before the tide goes out again, and they navigate by following the trail of mucus which they left on the way out. Some sort of memory has also been suggested. Large limpets have an intriguing method of defending themselves against predatory starfish. They will apparently lift up their shell and slam the edge down on the starfish's arm or tube feet. The three different species of *Patella* (*P. vulgata* the common limpet, *P. ulyssiponensis* the china limpet and *P. depressa* the black-footed limpet) are difficult to distinguish without removing them from their rock and this can maim or kill them. [Shell up to 6 cm long]

# Blue-rayed limpet  -  *Helcion pellucidum*

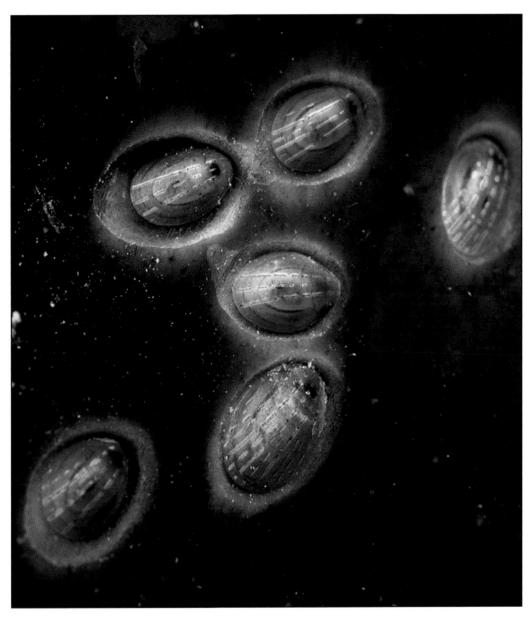

This beautiful little animal is only found on kelp plants, so it is often overlooked by divers and snorkellers to whom the swaying forests of kelp appear relatively unappealing. The delicate, slightly translucent shell is usually kelp coloured and would be unremarkable if it was not marked by broken lines of a wonderful kingfisher blue. The limpets are often found in small groups and each one excavates its own little pit into the kelp frond or stalk as it feeds. Some of these limpets appear to move down the kelp as autumn approaches, so they avoid being cast adrift when the frond is lost or damaged in winter storms. A different variety of the same species has a rougher shell with less prominent blue markings, and lives down in the holdfast of the kelp. [Shell up to 2 cm across]

## Painted top-shell - *Calliostoma zizyphinum*

The shell of this mollusc is in the shape of a sharply-pointed, straight-sided cone. Shell colouration is usually an attractive yellowish pink with streaks and blotches of crimson or brown. Completely white individuals may also be found. The animal apparently keeps its shell clean by regularly rubbing it with its extendable foot. Like all top-shells, *Calliostoma* is a grazer and feeds on algae and other tiny organisms that live on the rock surfaces over which it crawls. In the summer, it can sometimes be found laying its long gelatinous egg ribbon which it attaches to stones or rock. This photograph shows a top-shell crawling up a kelp stem. The animal's foot, with its associated tentacles extending up onto the shell, can clearly be seen. [Shell up to 3 cm across]

## Auger (or tower) shell - *Turritella communis*

These very distinctive long, pointed and screw-like shells are often found empty and strewn across a sandy seabed; or in use as the jauntily-carried homes of small hermit crabs. When the original mollusc owner is in residence, the shell lies buried just under the surface of muddy sand where

its shape helps it to stay screwed into position. The animal is well adapted to this sedentary lifestyle and simply pumps in seawater from which it extracts oxygen and filters out particles of food. A cluster of the auger shell's egg capsules can be seen in the photograph as sandy-coloured beads attached to their stalk. To the left of the picture, are a sand-mason worm (page 68) and a burrowing anemone (page 45). [Shell up to 5 cm long]

## Edible periwinkle - *Littorina littorea*

Edible periwinkles are widespread and found in huge numbers on the shore and in shallow water. Usually thought of as rocky coast animals, they also live in muddy areas such as estuaries. The shell is shaped like that of a snail and is coloured black, grey or dark brown. Several similar types of periwinkle, including other species of the *Littorina* genus, are also very common and are distinguished by their different shell features and colours. All periwinkles are herbivorous grazers but the various species have quite different life histories. The eggs of some (including the edible periwinkle) float in open water and develop into planktonic larvae, while the eggs of others are attached to the seabed and hatch into miniature versions of the adults. Some species even brood their eggs internally and then give birth to fully-

formed periwinkles. [Edible periwinkle shell up to 3 cm across, most other types are smaller]

## Slipper limpet - *Crepidula fornicata*

Now widespread around the south of Britain, this species was accidentally introduced from America back in the 19th century. It arrived in a shipment of oysters which were then re-laid for fattening on British oyster beds. The shell is a flattish oval shape and has a large shelf across its opening, visible when turned over (see top photograph), which gives it the appearance of a slipper. Its most remarkable feature is the way in which it forms stacks of up to twelve individuals (the bottom photograph shows a stack of four). Larger stacks tend to be curved like an arch, hence the specific name of *fornicata*, Latin for arch. The large limpets at the bottom of a chain are female, the small ones at the top are

Shell opening with shelf, producing the "slipper" shape

Stack of four limpets

male and the ones in between are, as one might suspect, in between. The animals change from male to female as they grow older. A young slipper limpet settling on its own develops into a female relatively rapidly, while one settling at the end of a chain will spend some time as a functional male. It appears that females secrete a sort of hormone into the water which maintains the masculinity of nearby males. The adult animals are immobile but males use their long penis to fertilise a female within the chain. Where there are dense masses of slipper limpets, near Weymouth for example, they seem to take over the sea floor. They are filter feeders and can be a serious pest to oyster beds through crowding and competition for planktonic food. [Shell up to 5 cm long]

# Large necklace shell (or moon snail) - *Euspira catena*

The foot of this attractive mollusc spreads up onto its shell when it is active, and also out across the sand like a skirt as it crawls along. Its rounded shell is glossy and an overall pale orange or fawn, with a row of brownish streaks running around the upper part of the spiral. The necklace shell preys on small clam-like bivalve molluscs that are buried in the sand. Having found the bivalve's siphons at the surface of the sand, it burrows down to attack. The bivalve shell is first softened chemically and then bored through with the necklace shell's drill-like radula. This leaves a neat round hole near the hinge that can often be seen on empty bivalve shells washed up on the beach. The spreading of the necklace shell's foot up around its shell makes it into a more streamlined form for burrowing. It is also useful in defence, as the tube feet of a predatory starfish cannot get a grip on the slimy tissue as easily as they could on a bare shell. Necklace shells lay a distinctive egg ribbon that looks just like a collar. Most of the eggs in the ribbon end up feeding the small proportion that develop. This species is found on sandy seabeds all around Britain, at virtually any depth. [Shell up to 3 cm tall]

## European cowrie - *Trivia monacha*

The cowrie's shell is shiny and appears highly polished but, in an active animal, it is almost completely obscured by folds of soft mantle tissue which extend from the entrance in the base of the shell. These folds have a rather striking pattern, a little like that of fake leopard-skin. The pale shell is traversed by delicate ribs and there are three dark blotches along its top (the blotches are absent

on the shell of the Arctic cowrie, *Trivia arctica*, a close relative). The European cowrie is more common in the south and west of Britain, with the Arctic cowrie more so in the north. Both species of cowrie eat colonial sea squirts, also laying their eggs in holes bitten out of the colonies. The photograph shows a European cowrie crawling across sand, but they are more commonly found on rocks and stones. [European cowrie, shell up to 1.5 cm long. Arctic cowrie, shell up to 1 cm]

## Dog-whelk - *Nucella lapillus*

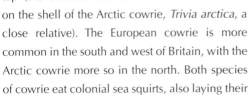

Dog-whelks are abundant on rocky beaches. Though small, the pale-coloured shell is quite heavily built to withstand the rigours of living on wave-battered shores. It usually bears obvious spiral ridges but these can be worn virtually smooth in some animals. The dog-whelk is an active carnivore, forcing open the top plates of barnacles or boring through the shells of mussels to feast on their soft insides. The boring process, which uses a combination of chemical softening and mechanical drilling or rasping, can take several hours. The dog-whelk's claim to fame in recent years has been as a sensitive indicator of pollution caused by tributyl tin (TBT) anti-fouling paint, which is used to prevent growth of encrusting creatures on boat hulls. Minute concentrations of TBT in seawater cause female

dogwhelks to develop male sexual organs and become sterile, causing severe damage to some populations. Legislation on the use of TBT has allowed some recovery. [Shell up to 4 cm long]

# Netted dog-whelk - *Hinia reticulata*

This animal is a very common sight on sand, particularly where there are rocks nearby. It has a conical shell, distinctively marked with a neat rectangular pattern (hence the name) formed by the interaction of flat ribs and spiral ridges. A long siphon is usually held aloft and draws water down to the animal for respiration, even when the shell is completely buried in the sand. The incoming water is also tested for evidence of carrion and these animals can detect food at a considerable distance. They are often found gathered in large numbers on a fish or crab carcass (see middle photograph) and a search of the sand nearby usually reveals several latecomers hurrying to the feast. The female lays very distinctive egg capsules in rows on eel-grass (see bottom photograph), seaweed or stones. They are shaped like tiny flattened vases and are transparent so the eggs can be seen inside. [Shell up to 3 cm long, egg capsules 0.5 cm tall]

Netted dog-whelks feeding on a crab carcass

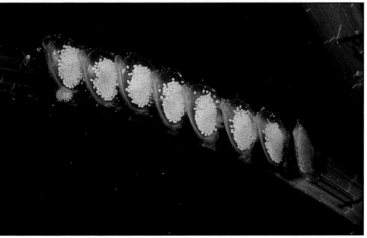

Egg capsules on eel-grass

# Whelk - *Buccinum undatum*

A "snail on steroids" might be an apt description for this hefty mollusc that is usually found on soft seabeds. The spiral shell is heavily built and covered with lines and ribs; and the body is whitish with often obvious black flecks. The back of the whelk's foot carries a flat oval of horny material that looks surplus to requirements when the animal is crawling along. When the whelk is threatened and retreats into its shell, the function of this item can be appreciated as a neat lid or door that bars the shell's entrance (see second photograph). Another method of self defence is employed when a whelk moves its body with a violent rocking motion to dislodge an attacking starfish. After mating, the female whelk will lay a mass of up to 2000 egg capsules attached to the seabed (see third photograph). Each capsule contains approximately 1000 eggs. The vast majority of eggs and embryos fail to reach maturity and are used as food by the lucky few who survive. The sandy-coloured bunches of empty egg capsules are often found washed up on the shore and are called "sea-wash balls" because they were once used like a sponge or flannel. Adult whelks eat sand-dwelling worms as they crawl across the

The shell "door" in use

seabed and also prey on bivalve molluscs, such as cockles, by forcing the shells apart with the edge of their own shell. They are also voracious consumers of dead and dying animals. It is the

A whelk egg mass

old shells of the whelk that are used by most large hermit crabs (pages 89-91) for their homes. [Shell up to 11 cm long]

# Sea hare - *Aplysia punctata*

The sea hare (along with *Pleurobranchus*, page 116 and *Philine*, page 117) is a sea slug, but has a much reduced shell that is hidden by the soft tissues. The other slugs described in this chapter are nudibranchs and have no shell at all. The sea hare has large flap-like lobes of tissue on its back and two pairs of tentacles on the head. The upper pair are broad, like hare's ears, hence the name. Colouration may be brown, olive-green or dark red, often with blackish spots and veining. Sea hares are herbivores and the type of seaweed they eat may affect their colour. Individuals eating the appropriately named food of sea lettuce are thought to be green, while those eating red seaweeds (usually younger sea hares) can be almost maroon. Many sea slugs secrete a noxious chemical as a defensive mechanism and the sea hare uses a two-part mixture of foul-tasting whitish slime and vivid purple fluid, each produced by separate glands. The sea hare is a

Mating chain and pink egg string

hermaphrodite like all sea slugs, and has a particularly interesting sex life. Although incapable of fertilising itself, any individual can act as either a male or female to another. Several sea hares will sometimes form a mating chain where each behaves as a male to the one below it and as a female to the one above. The smaller photograph shows such a chain and also a pink strand of sea hare eggs. [Up to 20 cm long but usually much smaller]

## *Pleurobranchus membranaceus*

Laying egg ribbon

This large sea slug has a pale brown body, usually with patches of darker brown, which is covered in soft tubercles that give it a "warty" appearance. Its mantle tissue forms a skirt around the body. The slug shown in the main photograph was in the midst of producing its coiled egg ribbon which may contain more than one million eggs. This species feeds on sea squirts by drilling through their tough outer tunic and sucking out the soft insides. Like the sea hare, it has an internal shell

Swimming

hidden by the soft tissues. With no protection offered by the shell, potential predators are deterred by sulphuric acid which is produced by the skin and released if it is broken. *Pleurobranchus* can swim well, always in an upside-down position, using undulating movements of its foot (smaller photograph). Very occasionally, huge populations have been witnessed undertaking swimming migrations. The purpose of these is a mystery but aggregation for mating seems to be the most likely reason. [Up to 12 cm long]

## *Philine aperta*

At first glance, this slightly nondescript looking sea slug can be mistaken for a piece of white debris lying on the seabed; but a trail left behind it in the form of a groove in the mud is often a sign of vitality. A closer look will reveal a soft and glossy white body that resembles a squashed egg. Like the sea hare and *Pleurobranchus* (pages 115-116) it is not a nudibranch and has an internal shell. *Philine aperta* can be abundant in muddy or sandy areas, where it burrows in search of worm and small mollusc prey. Its skin produces

sulphuric acid to ward off predators, but it is thought to be eaten by haddock and flatfish. [Up to 7 cm long]

## *Tritonia hombergi*

Despite being the largest nudibranch sea slug in British waters, *Tritonia hombergi* can be surprisingly difficult to spot. The numerous branched protrusions (gills) around its white or pinkish brown body help it to blend in with its surroundings, particularly as it is usually found with dead men's fingers (pages 50-51). It feeds on this soft coral and apparently on nothing else. The rounded bumps on its back produce an irritant compound that has been found to cause skin blisters on some people handling it. *Tritonia hombergi*, like all British sea

*Tritonia* amongst kelp and brittle stars

slugs for which there is information, lives no longer than a year. [Up to 20 cm long]

## *Lomanotus genei*

Mating pair

Like *Tritonia* (page 117) and all the sea slugs after this, the wonderfully flamboyant *Lomanotus* is a nudibranch and lacks a shell entirely. Its colour can vary from white through pink and orange to red, but it is characterised by a distinctive frill of protuberances with yellow or orange tips along the body. The main photograph shows a mating pair. As is typical with nudibranchs, the pair manage to both act as male and female during mating, thus fertilising each other simultaneously. The smaller photograph shows a single animal for ease of recognition. *Lomanotus* feeds on hydroids and winds its egg string around them at

spawning time. It can swim clumsily if disturbed. [Up to 9 cm long]

## *Okenia elegans*

Laying eggs

The body of this beautiful nudibranch sea slug is basically white, but may have such dense red freckles that it appears pink. There is a brilliant yellow border around the base of the body and the gills and various body protuberances are also splashed with yellow. The pair of tentacles, known as rhinophores, on the upper side of the head are highly convoluted and patterned in red and white with pale tips. The photographs show a pink slug laying its eggs and a virtually white individual crawling across the sea bed. *Okenia* feeds on sea squirts by burrowing into them, so it is often only the tips of the feathery gills that can be seen. It is usually classified as a rare species but can be quite common in locations such as

Plymouth Sound and Torbay. Most sightings come from south west Britain. [Up to 8 cm long]

## *Onchidoris bilamellata*

This species may appear drab in comparison to its more flamboyant nudibranch sea slug colleagues, but the large aggregations it can form are impressive in their own right. The slug's body is a basic off-white but there is usually a dense brown blotchy pattern on its back. Numerous small projections all over the body tend to show through as off-white bumps. The head bears a pair of obvious ridged head tentacles (rhinophores) and there is a crown of feathery gills at the rear of the body. These slugs feed on barnacles and can occur in dense gatherings where their prey is plentiful, such as on a seabed of barnacle-encrusted stones and boulders. The top "lid" plates of the barnacles are chewed away so that the soft inner body is sucked out, leaving an empty base. Because the empty bases are paler than intact barnacles, an area recently ravaged by these slugs has quite a distinctive appearance. The aggregations shown in the photographs were found near Oban in August; many of the

Aggregation of sea slugs with their egg ribbons (both photographs)

individuals were mating and ribbons of eggs were scattered over the seabed. Acidic defensive secretions are produced by this species if it is disturbed. A closely related but smaller species, *Onchidoris muricata*, feeds on bryozoans and is shown on page 139. [*O. bilamellata* up to 4 cm long, *O. muricata* up to 1.5 cm long]

## Diaphorodoris luteocincta

The colouration of this small nudibranch sea slug species is both conspicuous and distinctive. Against an overall background of white, there is a large red blotch down the centre of its back and a yellow rim around the edge of its body. It has a similar form to *Onchidoris bilamellata* and, like that species, the bumps on its back

appear white through the darker blotching. *Diaphorodoris luteocincta* feeds on particular species of bryozoans and is usually found on the silt covered rocks where these thrive. The pair in the photograph had probably just mated or were about to mate. [Up to 1 cm long]

## Acanthodoris pilosa

Its "fluffy" appearance is a characteristic of this common species. This impression arises from the long and soft protrusions on its body surface, which contrast with the more rounded bumps of several other species of nudibranch. The head tentacles (rhinophores) are club-shaped and there is a large crown of gills at its rear. Colour can be

white or any shade of brown through to black, or even purple. The usual prey of this slug includes the bryozoan (*Alcyonidium diaphanum*) known as sea chervil. The photograph (small, left) on page 140 shows the sea slugs and their eggs on a colony of the bryozoan. [Up to 5 cm long]

## Polycera faeroensis

The translucent white body of this nudibranch (common in the south and west) tends to appear slightly swollen. Various parts of it are splashed with bright yellow, such as the distinctive tapering extensions around the front of the head (of which there are eight or more). There is also yellow on the tips of the pair of tentacles on top of the head, on the gills towards the rear, and on the protuberances next to them. A closely related and more widespread species, *Polycera quadrilineata*, is similar in appearance but has fewer tapering extensions at the very front of the head (usually four) and splashes of yellow or orange forming several lines down the body itself. [Up to 5 cm long]

## Limacia clavigera

A small white nudibranch with yellow or orange marking on the bumps and finger-like protuberances round its head and down the back of its body. The more rounded shape and form of these protuberances distinguish this species from *Polycera faeroensis* (above). It feeds on encrusting bryozoans such as the sea-mat (page 139). The pair in the photograph were resting on a mesh-like sea-mat colony and were in the process of mating. It can be seen that the sexual organs on the right-hand side of the slugs' bodies are joined so that there is mutual fertilisation. [Up to 2 cm long]

Pair mating

# Sea lemon - *Archidoris pseudoargus*

The sea lemon is a large nudibranch, very common all around Britain. The upper side of its body is covered in small wart-like bumps and usually bears blotchy markings which can be any combination of yellow, pink, white, brown or green. A ring of feathery gills sticks up from near the animal's rear but is retracted quickly on the sensing of any disturbance. Sea lemons feed exclusively on encrusting sponges, chiefly the breadcrumb sponge (page 20), and their seemingly garish colouration can actually make them extremely difficult to spot when they are crawling across a mass of sponge. The smaller photograph shows a sea lemon's egg ribbon, which is laid in a coil with its bottom edge attached to the substrate, so a characteristic rosette is formed. Another

Slug laying egg ribbon and completed rosette

ribbon is being laid in the background. The sea lemon's entire life cycle is completed within a year. Adults mate and spawn in the spring before dying, and the new juveniles appear in the late summer and grow through the autumn and winter. [Up to 12 cm long]

## *Janolus cristatus*

This species, while not as colourful as some of its relatives, is still particularly striking. The pale translucent body is covered by numerous finger-like projections that appear rather bloated. A thin dark thread of digestive gland runs down the centre of each projection, sometimes forming tributaries near its end. There are splashes of an iridescent bluish-white pigment on the tips of the projections, and also in patches on the rest of the body.

It is a fairly widespread animal, but is thought to be restricted to calm water because of its fragility. Its eggs look like a wavy string of tiny white beads reminiscent of a miniature pearl necklace; each bead contains around 250 individual eggs. [Up to 8 cm long]

## *Flabellina pedata*

This is a small nudibranch but one with fabulous colouration. The body is an overall pink-purple and the projections along its back have bright white markings at their tips. The eggs are laid as a thin white thread that is sometimes easier to spot than the sea slugs themselves because, despite

their bright colours, they can be overlooked when amongst reddish seaweeds. The species is widespread, being found all around Britain and on most coasts between Norway and the Mediterranean. [Usually up to 2 cm long, but occasionally larger]

## *Coryphella browni*

The body of this nudibranch is a translucent white but the numerous long and pointed projections, or cerata, on its back contain brightly coloured (usually crimson) tributaries of the digestive gland. There is also a broad and very obvious white band near the tip of each projection. *Coryphella browni* feeds on hydroids such as the oaten pipe (page 56) and can often be found munching away at their polyps while perched on the straw-like stems (see photograph). Not only is it undeterred by their stinging abilities, it is one of the nudibranchs that ingests the stinging cells of such animals and puts them to its own use. The slug passes the intact cells through its digestive system and out to the cerata tips, where they are used for defence against predators. A hungry fish that attacks the slug is almost bound to nip the cerata, causing stinging cells to discharge and the attack to be abandoned. Egg masses of this species, which look like wavy white threads, are often laid amongst the hydroid stems. Several other nudibranch species, some of which belong to the same *Coryphella* genus, have a very similar appearance. [Up to 5 cm long]

# Common mussel - *Mytilus edulis*

Close-up of mussel showing siphons

The common mussel's curved, two-halved shell in blue, black and brown is instantly recognisable. Mussels normally live in large aggregations on the shore or in shallow water; the photograph opposite shows such a mussel bed in Loch Creran, west Scotland. They anchor themselves to the rocks and each other with sticky threads called byssus. These threads are planted, like the guy ropes of a tent, by the highly extendable foot which can reach out some distance from the shell (see smaller photograph on this page, taken in an aquarium). Like all bivalve molluscs, mussels filter suspended food out of the water in which they live. Water is pumped in via the frilly-edged opening, and leaves by the smooth-edged outflow tube. These siphons are both visible when the shells are gaping (see main photograph on this page). Despite their tough shells, mussels have a large number of predators and may be pulled open by starfish, broken open by crabs or drilled into by dog-whelks. They can even be attacked from inside by tiny pea crabs who ride in on their

Mussel in centre has foot extended

feeding current and then stay there to live in a permanent larder. Mussels can only offer passive resistance to most predators but they take an active stance against the dog-whelk. While the dog-whelk is preoccupied with drilling, a task that may take hours or even days, the victim and its mussel neighbours may attach so many byssus threads to its shell that it is turned over or at least immobilised. The dog-whelk will then eventually starve to death. [Shell up to 10 cm long but usually much smaller]

# Common mussel - *Mytilus edulis*

A mussel bed is also a home for other animals such as gobies, barnacles, crabs, periwinkles and dog-whelks

127

## Horse mussel - *Modiolus modiolus*

The horse mussel is usually larger than the common mussel and is a lot more heavily built. Its bulky appearance is given perspective by the helpfully positioned crab (carrying eggs) in the photograph. The narrower end of the horse mussel's shell is also very rounded, in contrast to the more pointed end of the common mussel, but this feature may well be hidden amongst the stones or mud where it lives. Only the broad end of the shell with the openings for water entry and exit are then visible. Horse mussels can occur in dense aggregations where, aided by their byssus (anchoring) threads, they stabilise and bulk up the seabed so that a type of reef is formed. Numerous other types of animal attach themselves to the horse mussels' shell surfaces (hydroids, bryozoans, sea squirts) or hide in the crevices between the shells (worms, crabs, brittle stars) making an extremely rich community. [Shell up to 20 cm long]

## Gaping file shell (or flame shell) - *Limaria hians*

This most striking of bivalves usually remains hidden inside a "nest" which is made of gravel and shell debris bound up with the file shell's own byssus (anchoring) threads. Together, many nests can form a file shell reef, a firm base where other sorts of animals can attach and make their home. The individual pictured here had been captured by a velvet swimming crab who was presumably going to try and break it open at the earliest opportunity. The crab might have been deterred, however, by the acid secretions that the file shell can produce. The attractive fringe of red/orange tentacles is always on display in this species, surrounding the

oval shell which is decorated with delicate ridges. It can swim actively when disturbed, using a jet of water expelled from its snapping shells (as in the scallops); this is assisted by rowing movements of the file shell's long tentacles. [Shell up to 3 cm long]

# Great (or king) scallop - *Pecten maximus*

Unlike those of the mussel and many bivalve molluscs, the great scallop's two shell halves differ greatly in shape. The lower is curved like a bowl, while the upper is flat, like a lid. Both halves bear distinctive radiating ribs. Scallops use a rocking motion to make a hollow for themselves in sand or gravel, where they sit with shells gaping as they filter feed. The attractive patterning on the soft tissue "curtain" can then be seen, along with the numerous small tentacles and tiny eyes with their metallic blue sheen. Scallops swim rather comically by rapidly snapping their shells, the soft tissues guiding the resulting water jets to give some control over direction. Tiring quickly, the swimming range is small, though quite enough to escape a predatory starfish. [Shell up to 15 cm across]

# Queen scallop - *Aequipecten opercularis*

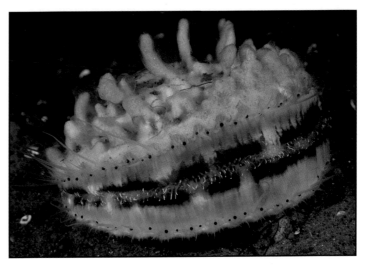

This bivalve is similar to the great (or king) scallop but, as its name suggests, tends to be smaller. A better distinguishing feature is that the upper half of its shell is curved like an upside down bowl, rather than flat like the great scallop's. The upper half is actually slightly more cupped than the lower. The queen scallop is a more vigorous swimmer than its larger relative but uses the same snapping motion. It will often swim several metres at a fair pace when disturbed or threatened by a predator. Growths of sponge are found on many queen scallop shells (see photograph) and this arrangement is thought to benefit both parties. The sponge is less likely to be grazed by a predator, such as the sea lemon sea slug (page 123), than if it was on a rock; and the sponge will help to keep starfish off the scallop. [Shell up to 10 cm across]

## Common cuttlefish - *Sepia officinalis*

The cuttlefish is one of the most fascinating animal encountered in our waters, and the next five pages are intended to introduce its intriguing nature. Very small individuals of this species could be confused with the little cuttle, *Sepiola*, (see page 135) but otherwise it is unmistakable. The broad and slightly flattened body, up to 30 cm long, is fringed by a fin on each side which runs from just behind the head right back to the rear. The mouth is surrounded by eight arms, two of which are sometimes raised above the head when approached. There are also two much longer, extendible tentacles hence the classification of decapod (ten feet). If startled, a cuttlefish may use its full **escape mechanism**, where the body assumes a shape for maximum streamlining and a powerful burst of jet propulsion thrusts it rapidly backwards. At the

same time, it can release a cloud of black ink which will hang in the water and momentarily distract a pursuer while the cuttlefish escapes. If still pursued, larger clouds of ink are poured out. Once used by artists, the ink was called sepia, as in the animal's Latin name. If not startled when first encountered, the cuttlefish may well move slowly away, using a little gentle jet propulsion aided and stabilised by the rippling motion of its fringing fins. It is then that their most impressive skill, the total **control of colour and patterning**, can be appreciated. They may be less famous for it, but cuttlefish are much more skilful colour-change artists than even chameleons. If a cuttlefish swims off over a varying sea bed, its shade can change instantly to match its surroundings, going dark over kelp-covered rocks and almost white over sand. The animal seems to

## Common cuttlefish - *Sepia officinalis*

calculate all the angles, apparently matching the seabed against which the observer is seeing it, rather than that directly below it. If it comes to rest on the bottom, it will blend in perfectly. The top photograph on this page shows a cuttlefish as it first comes to sit on a gravel seabed; a few seconds later (middle photograph) it has matched the gravel perfectly. To further improve **camouflage**, projections on the skin's surface will change its texture to replicate that of the surroundings. Cuttlefish will also flick sand or gravel up over themselves and gradually sink into the seabed, leaving only the tops of their heads and backs exposed (see page 8). When in such a position, only the most sharp-eyed diver will spot them. In addition to simply matching their surroundings, cuttlefish use all sorts of patterns in an attempt to break up their outline and generally confuse potential predators. From birth, young cuttlefish can display at least thirteen types of **body pattern**, made up from over thirty different components. Whatever the exact purpose of them all, and even the scientists who have logged them remain unsure of this, watching a cuttlefish

This cuttlefish has just settled on a gravel sea bed

A few seconds later, it has matched its background

Another individual, showing the white square pattern

## Common cuttlefish - *Sepia officinalis*

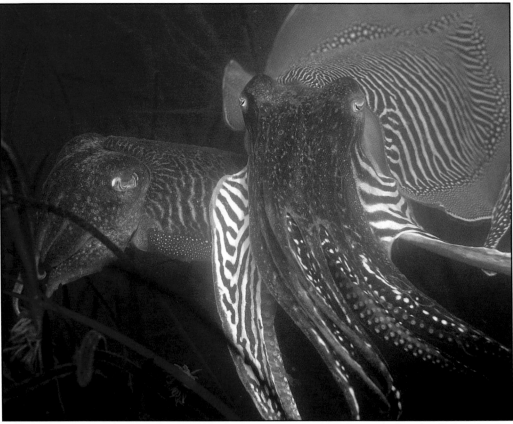

A courting couple, the male with dramatic stripes

flash through part of its repertoire is an awe-inspiring sight. One of the most common patterns is known as the "white square" (bottom photograph, previous page) which is accompanied by a white stripe on the head and a small white triangle at the rear. The secret of **rapid pattern change** is explained by the presence of special cells, known as chromatophores, within cuttlefish skin. These are effectively little flexible bags of pigment which, when expanded by muscular action, make the area of skin appear dark. When the bags are allowed to contract under the power of their own elasticity, the skin appears pale. In addition to avoiding predators, pattern control is also used in **courtship**. Male cuttlefish display brilliant zebra stripes at courting time in order to impress females and warn off

competitors (see above). Mating is achieved by the male passing the female a packet of sperm, using one of his arms specially adapted for the purpose. After mating, a male will often defend the female while she lays her eggs, though there can be a delay of several days. **Clumps of eggs**, dyed black with ink and known as "sea grapes", can be seen attached to seaweed or eel-grass in the summer months (top photograph, opposite page). The eggs hatch after two to three months and miniature cuttlefish, around finger-nail size, emerge (middle photograph, opposite page). As mentioned earlier, the junior cuttlefish immediately show good powers of patterning control. Even so, they are very vulnerable to predators, and mortality at this stage in their life is high. Females only breed once and die soon after

## Common cuttlefish - *Sepia officinalis*

laying their eggs. Unlike their relative the octopus, they take no care of them. After cuttlefish have died and decomposed, their internal skeleton or **cuttlebone** (bottom photograph, this page) is often found washed up on beaches. In life, this is the animal's buoyancy organ and it consists of stacks of thin-walled chambers that can be filled with either liquid or gas in order to give precisely the right degree of lift. Cuttlefish spend the winter in relatively deep water, such as that in the western English Channel, though they cannot inhabit very deep water because the cuttlebone could implode under high pressure. They move into shallow coastal waters to breed in the spring and summer. It is then that divers can see them in large numbers, and snorkellers may even see them close to the shore. Numbers of cuttlefish found inshore at particular locations fluctuate markedly, with large numbers being seen in some years and hardly any in others. Cuttlefish are **impressive predators**, able to catch fast moving prey such as fish or prawns with their long tentacles. The arms, along with the razor-sharp beak hidden behind them, also enable a pugnacious

Cuttlefish eggs

A new hatchling

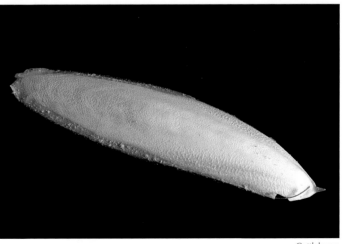

Cuttlebone

## Common cuttlefish - *Sepia officinalis*

Familiar gesture by cornered cuttlefish

crab to be turned into a meal in seconds. If a cuttlefish's approach is met by a crab with defiantly raised claws, it will simply grab it from the rear. Aside from sea mammals, cuttlefish (along with octopus) are undoubtedly the most **intelligent** creatures a diver will meet. Encounters leave you with the impression that you have been observed as much as observing! The individual being watched in the photograph above has extended its two long tentacles, a gesture sometimes seen in situations when a cuttlefish might feel cornered. Is it an attempt at communication? [Up to 30 cm long]

# Little cuttle - *Sepiola atlantica*

The little cuttle, *Sepiola*, has the appearance of a miniature *Sepia*. It is very difficult to spot underwater and only close inspection will reveal that it is a rather different shape to its larger relative. The body is cup-shaped and there is a pair of lobe-like fins that do not run the entire length of the body. Other characteristic features include its very protrusive eyes and the greenish tinge to the tops of the eye bulges. The little cuttle's buoyancy control system is less sophisticated than that of the common cuttlefish but it can hover effectively or jet away quickly. The tiny clouds of ink released by this species when disturbed appear quite comical to the diver, but can still be used effectively in combination with colour control. By discharging a dark cloud of ink at the same moment that they jet away, and by turning their body from dark to pale, a predator's attention can be distracted to follow the ink cloud and the cuttle can escape unnoticed. The photograph above shows the role of individual colour cells (chromatophores) in cuttlefish pattern control. In the middle of the body, the cells are expanded forming dark discs. In the near part of the rear, they are contracted into small spots so the skin appears mainly white. Little cuttles live on sandy bottoms and spend much of the time partly buried with only their eyes exposed, watching for predators or hapless small crustaceans which they will capture on emerging from the sand. [Up to 5 cm long]

## Lesser (or curled) octopus - *Eledone cirrhosa*

The octopus may be one of those animals usually associated with warmer climes but this species can be a regular sighting for observant divers in many areas of Britain. Like all octopods, it has a **soft bag-like body** which contains no skeletal support (unlike its cuttlefish relatives which have the cuttlebone) and eight long sucker-bearing arms. That body can be moulded into virtually any shape and squeezed through the tiniest crevice in an attempt to catch prey or evade a predator such as a conger eel, cod or sea mammal. An octopus will often remain hidden in a hole or crevice during the day. The smaller photograph on the opposite page shows an octopus at the entrance to its home, with an eye and part of its body visible; an arm is spread out to partially cover the entrance. If an octopus itself cannot be seen, empty crab carcasses near the lair may give its presence away. Crabs, which form a large part of their **diet**, are enveloped in the arms of the octopus, pierced by their sharp jaws and killed by injected poison. Digestive enzymes are pumped in and the resulting crab "soup" is sucked out. The larger photograph on the opposite page shows an octopus just finishing off its meal of an edible crab and discarding the pieces of empty shell. Although they don't simply shed eggs and sperm into the seawater like many marine animals, the **coupling** of octopods does not appear to be an intimate affair. The timid lovers seem to keep as far apart as possible and the male caresses the female with an outstretched

## Lesser (or curled) octopus - *Eledone cirrhosa*

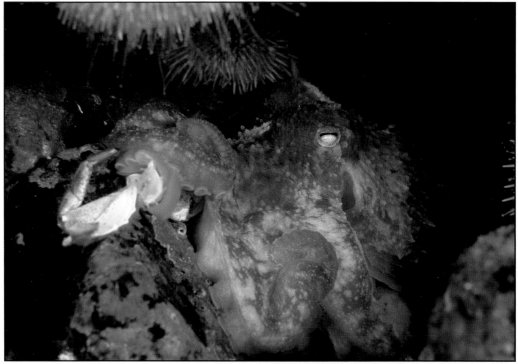

An octopus finishes off its meal of an edible crab and discards the remains

arm before inserting packages of sperm into her egg ducts. One of the male's arms is specially adapted for this purpose. The female octopus lays her eggs in large bunches within rock crevices or beneath stones. She stays to guard them until they hatch, hosing them with water from her funnel to keep them clean and aerated. The **devoted mother** barely feeds during this vigil

Octopus hiding in crevice, small spider crabs lurk nearby

and may well die soon after it is completed. Like cuttlefish, octopus are extremely intelligent. When kept in aquaria, they can learn their way around mazes in order to get food. A distinguishing feature of the lesser (or curled) octopus is that there is only a single row of suckers on each arm. The larger common octopus (*Octopus vulgaris*) has a double row of suckers and is found occasionally on the south coast of England; this representing the northern extent of its range. [Lesser octopus arm span up to 70 cm; common octopus arm span up to 3 m]

# Chapter 7
# BRYOZOANS

## Sea mosses

A number of marine animals resemble plants but bryozoans take this to the extreme, with the pale brown growths of many species looking just like poorly seaweed at first glance. Bryozoa means "moss animal" and members of this phylum are sometimes called "sea mosses".

## Hairy tentacles

Bryozoans are stationary colonies of tiny animals called zooids. Most of these zooids are specialised for feeding and each has a ring of tentacles which surrounds its mouth, so it looks a little like a hydroid or miniature sea anemone. However there are no stinging cells (as there are on hydroid and sea anemone tentacles) and the bryozoans' tentacles are instead equipped with numerous hairs called cilia. These cilia beat rapidly and produce currents which carry microscopic organisms, such as bacteria and single-celled algae, into the bryozoan's mouth. There is a U-shaped digestive tract to process this food, and any undigested remains pass out of the anus which is positioned just outside the ring of tentacles.

## Living in a box

Each individual zooid lives in its own case, less than 1 mm across, which is usually shaped like a box. The walls of this box are often reinforced with calcium compounds. Numerous boxes joined together in the colony produce the mesh-like appearance that is so characteristic of bryozoans. The tentacles which protrude from each box can be seen when there is active feeding underway, but they are withdrawn instantly at the slightest disturbance.

## Specialisation and reproduction

Within most bryozoan colonies, there are zooids with specialisms other than feeding. Some attach their colony to the seabed, while others defend the colony against the larvae of other creatures that may settle on it or against larger animals (such as worms) that may crawl over it and cause damage. There are also zooids that specialise in reproduction. All bryozoan colonies are hermaphroditic (male and female at the same time) but some species have separate male and female zooids within a colony, while others have zooids that produce both eggs and sperm. Fertilised eggs are usually brooded within the colony and the resulting larvae swim for a few hours before finding a suitable place in which to settle. Each larva can transform into a zooid that then buds (reproduces asexually) to produce more zooids and form a large colony.

# Sea-mat - *Membranipora membranacea*

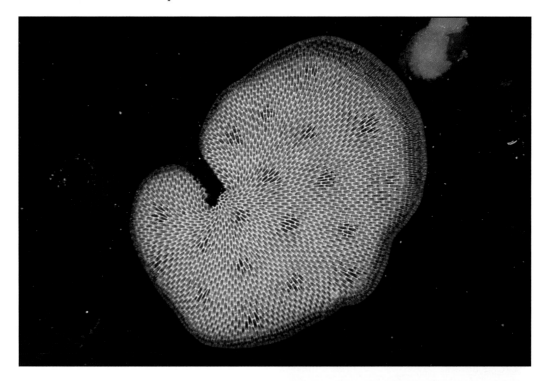

The distinctive colonies of the sea-mat are seen as a layer of fine lacy mesh on fronds of seaweed, particularly kelp. Though tiny, the individual rectangular "boxes" that make up the colony are clearly visible. Arranged in rows like brickwork, they give the colony enough flexibility to cope with bending of the kelp frond. The main photograph shows a colony just a few cm across, but they can cover much larger areas and spread rapidly by budding. By growing near the base of the frond, a colony ensures that it will not all be lost if the kelp frond becomes damaged and loses material from its outer edges. Several species of sea slugs (such as *Onchidoris muricata* shown in the bottom photograph, see also page 120) feed specifically on this bryozoan. Such mesh-encrusted fronds in shallow water are a good place to find a variety of sea slugs and their eggs. ["Boxes" less than a mm across but colonies can cover large areas of a kelp frond]

Sea slug feeding on sea-mat

Sea chervil and hornwrack growing in the Menai Straits

## Sea chervil - *Alcyonidium diaphanum*

## Hornwrack - *Flustra foliacea*

Sea chervil is easy to recognise although its fleshy texture and finger-like growths make it look more like a sponge than a typical bryozoan. Usually brownish in colour and with wavy surfaces, the fingers can be branched and are often found in bunches. The slightest amount of tide or current tends to push the bunches almost flat to the seabed on which they are attached. The sea slug, *Acanthodoris pilosa*, eats this species of bryozoan and lays its white egg ribbons on the fingers (see slug and eggs in the small photograph above, also the slug on page 121). Sea chervil is said to cause a type of skin irritation known as "Dogger Bank itch" by fishermen in the North Sea. [Fingers up to 50 cm long]

The frond-like colonies of hornwrack can cover quite large areas of rocky seabed in current-swept areas although their drab beige colour means they might not grab your attention. Pieces are often washed up on beaches where they look just like pale dried seaweed; but the telltale bryozoan "mesh" pattern can be made out on both dead pieces and on live growths underwater. Colonies only grow for part of the year so annual growth lines can sometimes be seen. This species is said to produce a characteristic lemon smell but this is not obvious in dried specimens or from inside a diving mask! The small photograph above was taken beneath the famous arch of Cathedral Rock at St Abbs. [Colonies up to 15 cm tall]

## Bugula plumosa

A number of bryozoan species, including several others which belong to the *Bugula* genus, occur as buff coloured colonies that can form a "turf" on rocks or other hard surfaces. These growths are easily overlooked but close inspection reveals that many of them have surprisingly attractive forms. The tuft-like colonies of *Bugula*

*plumosa* are shaped rather like tiny Christmas trees, but with their branches arranged in a spiral. Colonies are often found in small groups and, like other bryozoans, are preyed upon by certain species of sea slugs. [Up to 8 cm tall]

## Ross coral - *Pentapora foliacea*

This distinctive species is not a coral of course, but it forms open mounds made up of stiff interlocking "leaves" so the overall effect is that of a coral head or a cabbage. A close look at the "leaves" reveals the typical fine mesh-like structure of a bryozoan. Colour can range from dark orange-brown to sandy buff, but part of

the mound may be overgrown by algae or hydroids. Many small animals can reside in the cavities formed between the "leaves". Ross (sometimes "rose") coral is most common in the west and south west of Britain. [Mounds up to 50 cm across]

# Chapter 8

# ECHINODERMS

## Starfish, brittle stars, sea urchins, sea cucumbers & feather stars

The name, echinoderm, means "spiny-skinned" and refers to the skeleton of these animals, which is composed of bony plates embedded in the body wall. These plates may protrude to form spines and take on very different forms in the various sub-groups. They are relatively loosely arranged in starfish for instance, but form a rigid structure in sea urchins. Echinoderms have no front or back end because they are based on what is called radial symmetry, rather than the bilateral symmetry of many familiar animals. Starfish, for example, are just as likely to lead with one arm as with any other, and have no need to turn their body when changing direction. Some urchins and sea cucumbers operate as though they have a front end, but their basic body plan is still based on radial symmetry. Most echinoderms have separate sexes (rather than being hermaphrodites) and release their eggs and sperm into the water, so that fertilisation is external. A planktonic larval phase usually follows. The diagram below shows a generalised starfish life cycle followed by several (but not all) common species. After spawning, a fertilised egg develops through various larval stages; the final one of which houses a miniature starfish. This stage attaches to the seabed and releases the young starfish that then grows to maturity.

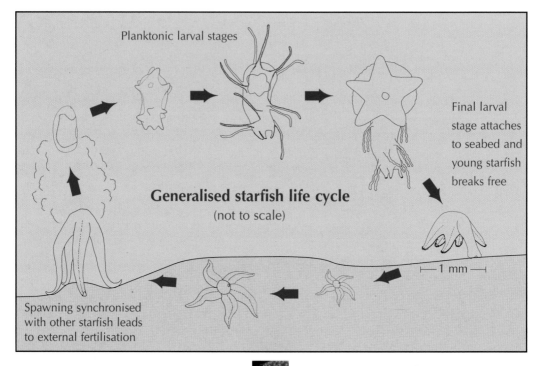

Planktonic larval stages

Final larval stage attaches to seabed and young starfish breaks free

**Generalised starfish life cycle**
(not to scale)

├─1 mm─┤

Spawning synchronised with other starfish leads to external fertilisation

Starfish close-up, showing tube feet, spines and pedicellariae

## Starfish features

The first thing you notice if you turn a starfish over is the huge number of tiny extendable legs, known as tube feet, bursting from the groove underneath each arm. All echinoderms have tube feet, operated by a special hydraulic system, even though they may be less conspicuous than those of starfish. Starfish tube feet are usually equipped with small suckers for gripping onto firm surfaces, and are used for walking the animal along and, in some species, for pulling open prey (see pages 145-146). The close-up photograph above shows the tube feet underneath the arm of a spiny starfish. It also shows the upper side of the arm, on which the prominent spines are surrounded by bunches of tiny structures, called pedicellariae, that have an intriguing function. Slow moving animals with a hard exterior can present an ideal home for encrusting animals, such as barnacles, looking for a free ride. The pedicellariae are like miniature pairs of jaws which, when touched by a small animal looking for somewhere to settle, will grasp it and kill it. Starfish have amazing regenerative powers. A single detached arm can produce a whole new starfish, as long as part of the central body is also present. This explains the bizarre shape of some individuals.

## Brittle stars

These animals look like emaciated starfish but have a different body layout because their arms are very clearly demarcated from the central disc. The bony plates of the arms form a continuous articulated armour which gives the whole arm the appearance of having joints. The arms are easily broken, hence the name, and can be jettisoned to permit escape from a predator, and then regenerated. Brittle stars move much more rapidly than starfish, using snake-like movements of their arms to propel them across the seabed. The tube feet simply give the arm some grip, rather than walking the animal along.

Various echinoderms on a gravel slope near Oban; common starfish, common sunstar, common sea urchin and feather stars

## Sea urchins

The bony plates possessed by sea urchins are more imposing than those of any other echinoderms and fit together to form a solid structure, known as a test. The usually impressive spines are mobile, being attached to the test with ball-and-socket joints, and they can help the tube feet with movement or be locked rigidly in position to anchor the urchin in a rock crevice. The tube feet are similar to those of starfish, though they are much longer in order to reach out beyond the spines.

## Sea cucumbers

These cucumber-shaped animals can be visualised as starfish with no arms that have grown extremely tall and thin. Some sea cucumbers, like the cotton-spinner, crawl over the bottom eating organic deposits. Others wedge themselves into rock crevices or burrow into soft sediments. From here, they hold out feeding tentacles, which are highly modified tube feet that surround their mouths, to catch suspended food. More conventional tube feet along the rest of the body help the cucumber with walking or burrowing. The skeleton of sea cucumbers is simply a few scattered bony elements in their leathery skin. As with other echinoderms however, the soft elements of the body wall can alter consistency, being soft when the cucumber needs to get through a narrow crack and then stiff when it needs to wedge itself in position.

## Feather stars

The aptly named feather stars have a long fossil history and are thought to be the most primitive echinoderms. The typical feather star features are described on page 166.

## Common starfish - *Asterias rubens*

The most familiar starfish to non-divers, it can be found on the lower shore and at virtually any depth, on sandy and stony seabeds as well as on rocks. It is usually orange or pale yellow/brown, sometimes red or purple, with a cream underside. The five (occasionally four or six) arms taper down towards their tips. The starfish's upper surface is covered with small blunt spines, with a marked line of larger spines down the middle of each arm. Belying their sluggish image, these starfish can be **fearsome predators** of bivalve molluscs such as mussels and clams. The top photograph on page 146 shows a starfish in characteristic feeding pose arched over a clam (the stripes on its shell are just discernible).

By using this position, it puts the maximum number of tube feet to work on pulling open the mollusc, and also positions its mouth right next to the crack between the shell halves. It is not clear whether a steady pull or a series of tugs is used, but the force applied by the tube feet has been estimated as being equivalent to 5 kg, and the hapless mollusc eventually tires. As soon as the tiniest crack appears between the shell halves, only a fraction of a millimetre across, the starfish pushes its stomach out through its mouth and slips it through this crack into the mollusc's interior. Digestive juices get to work and the battle is over. Common starfish can congregate in **large aggregations** where food is plentiful and

## Common starfish - *Asterias rubens*

Feeding on a clam

A mussel bed under attack

## Common starfish - *Asterias rubens*

Preparing to spawn

Spawning

## Common starfish - *Asterias rubens*

Righting itself

can be serious pests to mussel or oyster fisheries. The bottom photograph on page 146 shows a mussel bed near St Abbs (south east Scotland) which was under heavy attack. Bright silvery spots among the mussels mark shells emptied by starfish. Past attempts by shellfish collectors to kill dredged up starfish by simply chopping them in half and throwing them back into the sea were doomed to failure, because each half starfish simply grew another half and carried on as before! As in most starfish, the sexes of this species are separate. **Fertilisation** takes place when females and males shed their eggs and sperm (respectively) into the seawater at the same time. A chemical released with the eggs is thought to inspire both males and females in the vicinity to start **spawning**. The top photograph on page 147 shows a starfish preparing to spawn, raised up onto its arm tips on a rocky ledge. Prominent positions are often sought, with the top of kelp fronds a favourite, and the bottom photograph on page 147 shows an individual in the midst of spawning while in such a location. The milky cloud can be seen drifting off in the current. The photograph on this page shows how a starfish can right itself by twisting its arms and pulling itself over with the versatile tube feet. [Up to 50 cm across but rarely more than 30 cm and usually smaller]

# Spiny starfish - *Marthasterias glacialis*

With its large body covered in conspicuous knobs and spines, the spiny starfish can be an impressive animal. Mainly restricted to the western side of Britain, it can be very common in rocky or sandy and muddy habitats. In meadows of red seaweed, their usual pale blue colouration makes them extremely easy to spot. They can also be grey, brown or white, the purple tips to the arms being most noticeable on white individuals. Although the arms of this species appear heavily armoured with three rows of large spines running their length, they are quite soft and will be readily jettisoned if hurt or over-handled. Fortunately, they can be regenerated and spiny starfish with a mixture of normal arms and smaller ones in the process of being re-grown are a common sight. The tiny pincer-like organs, pedicellariae, are particularly prominent in this species and form obvious cushion-like wreaths around the large spines (see close-up photograph on page 143). Spiny starfish are voracious predators and, in addition to preying on bivalve molluscs, eat crustaceans, fish and other echinoderms such as starfish and sea urchins, dead or alive. [Up to 80 cm across but usually much smaller]

# Northern starfish - *Leptasterias muelleri*

This species looks rather like a small version of the common or spiny starfish (pages 145-149). It is, however, more spiny than the common starfish and lacks the obvious wreaths around the spines possessed by the spiny starfish. A clear line of spines can be seen down each arm in this young starfish. In older individuals, the spines are more randomly scattered. The northern starfish is usually purplish, becoming paler near the tips of the arms, but individuals found on the shore or in shallow water may be green. This is due to algae living in their tissues. As the name suggests, it is

found mainly around the north of Britain. This photograph was taken off Anglesey where it appeared to be quite common. [Usually no more than 10 cm across, often smaller]

# Bloody Henry - *Henricia oculata*

Common in wave or current swept rocky areas on southern and western coasts, the bloody Henry has an upper side that is usually coloured a dramatic pink, purple or crimson, and which has a rough sandpaper-like texture. The underside is a pale sandy colour. It has quite a different appearance from the common, spiny and northern starfish, because its five arms are round in cross-section, lack any obvious spines and look stiffer than those of the other species. It is a suspension feeder for at least some of the time, raising its arms up to catch food particles, and also browses on sponges. It has a smaller stomach than the more predatory starfish. An almost identical species, *Henricia sanguinolenta*, has a

more northern distribution so the two species probably overlap on the west coast of Scotland. [Up to 20 cm across]

# Common sunstar - *Crossaster papposus*

Though they possess many more arms than "standard" starfish, sunstars are very similar to them in basic form. The very striking common sunstar can have anything from 8 to 14 arms, but 10 to 12 is the most usual. The upper surface of the body and arms is very spiny and there are distinctive brush-like spines around the edges of the arms which create a rather "jagged" appearance. Colouration can be dull brown, but it is usually brilliant red or orange with pale bands on the arms that produce an impression of concentric rings like a target. The small white spot, often visible off-centre on the body, is the sieve plate (madreporite) which is the opening into the hydraulic system. This species is a voracious predator, eating a wide variety of animals. Other echinoderms such as starfish and sea cucumbers are a significant part of the diet. The common sunstar can be found all around Britain but is rarely seen on the south coast. This photograph also shows daisy anemones (page 39) and light-bulb sea squirts (page 170). [Up to 35 cm across]

# Purple sunstar - *Solaster endeca*

The purple sunstar is only found in the north of Britain. It has a rough upper surface but the spines are much less obvious than in the common sunstar. There are usually 9 or 10 arms, but this can vary from 7 to 13. Colour is normally a vibrant pink-purple but, despite the name, pale orange or cream-coloured individuals are also common. The paler coloured tips to the arms are often curled up, as on this large sunstar found on the silt-covered wreck of the Shuna in the Sound of Mull (main photograph). Like the common sunstar, this species is a voracious predator on other echinoderms. The two smaller photographs show a sunstar that, when turned over, was found to be eating a surprisingly large sea cucumber. After a quick look, it was turned back over and left to get on with its meal. [Up to 40 cm across]

Hunched up in feeding posture......

......a sea cucumber is being consumed

## Cushion star - *Asterina gibbosa*

The relatively large central portion and short blunt arms of this cushion star give it an almost pentagonal shape. It is usually much smaller than the other starfish described here, and is mainly found on the shore or in very shallow water. The upper surface of its body is rough, covered in small bundles of short spines. These spines, and those around the edges of the arms, are usually orange but the overall colour is quite variable, ranging from green or brown through to cream. Most starfish have entirely separate sexes but members of this species start out as males and become females later in life. It is a scavenger of dead plant and animal matter and is found only on western and southern coasts of Britain. [Up to 5 cm across]

## Red cushion star - *Porania pulvillus*

With its short arms, plump stature and velvet-like appearance, this creature really lives up to the name of cushion star. It is usually brilliant red, with scatterings of translucent small soft projections on its back, and some additional creamy-coloured markings. It occurs all around Britain, except for much of the North Sea coast, but I have only ever seen it on the west coast of Scotland. Often found on soft corals such as dead men's fingers (as here) on which it is thought to feed. [Up to 12 cm across]

# Seven armed starfish - *Luidia ciliaris*

A relatively primitive starfish, *Luidia ciliaris* has a distinctive appearance, although its orange colouration is shared by other species. The seven long arms are rather soft and only start to taper near their tips. A very prominent fringe of white spines runs round the edge of each arm. Unlike the majority of starfish, its

tube feet end in tiny knobs rather than suckers (see smaller photograph). *Luidia* is found on both sandy and stony sea beds all around Britain except for the southern part of the east coast. It can move surprisingly quickly and feeds mainly on other echinoderms such as brittle stars, starfish and urchins. An adult can apparently produce over two hundred million eggs in a year, so mortality at the egg and planktonic larval stages must be enormous. [Up to 60 cm across]

# Sand star - *Astropecten irregularis*

This burrowing species has a classic star shape with five rigid arms that taper noticeably along their entire length. Each arm is fringed with long pale spines and normally has a purple spot at its tip. The overall colour is typically a pinkish sandy hue though this may vary. With a much more flattened body than most starfish, and with pointed instead of sucker-bearing tube feet, the sand star is well adapted for burrowing into soft sediments. While burrowing, it is thought to eat shellfish, crustaceans and worms encountered along the way. Sand stars can also be encountered moving over the surface of a sandy seabed and they may consume small fish if these are slowed down by ill health. The sequence of photographs shows an individual disappearing into the sand over a period of only about 30 seconds. Rather than sliding down edge-on into the sand as might have been expected, it sank straight downwards. [Up to 15 cm across]

Sand star burrowing into the seabed

## Common brittle star  -  *Ophiothrix fragilis*

Common brittle stars, with arms raised for catching suspended food

### Common brittle star - *Ophiothrix fragilis*

This brittle star has flexible arms covered in long glassy spines which give them a very bristly appearance. The central body also bears spines, as visible on the animals at the bottom of the photograph opposite. Colouration is very variable, with red, yellow and blue often mixed in with brown and grey. The arms almost always have alternating light and dark bands. It is usually found amongst or under rocks, sometimes forming huge aggregations in deep water (see photograph above). Within these, up to 10,000 brittle stars per square metre have been recorded. The brittle stars' arms are raised up into the passing current where their tube feet

filter out suspended food matter, which is then passed along the arms to the central mouth. If the current gets too strong, the brittle stars link arms to form a huge mat that is less likely to get swept away. [Up to 20 cm across]

### Crevice brittle star - *Ophiopholis aculeata*

The crevice brittle star lives up to its name and is usually found partially hidden in a rocky crevice or beneath a boulder with just the arms protruding. The arms are distinctive because they tend to be twisted up rather than lying out straight, and are usually marked with banding. The central disc is covered with a pattern of large plates, separated by granules.

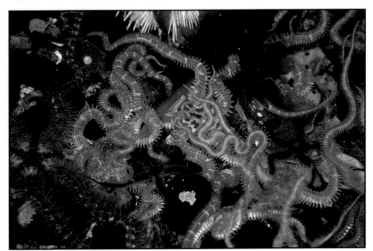

Crevice brittle stars (most obvious) with common and black brittle stars also present

Overall colour is typically reddish or purplish brown. The arm banding is obvious on the individuals in this photograph; also present are common brittle stars (on the left with very prominent glassy spines) and black brittle stars (coloured black and dark brown). The crevice brittle star is much more common in the north of Britain than in the south. [Up to 15 cm across]

# Black brittle star - *Ophiocomina nigra*

A distinctive species that appears clearly different from the common brittle star, because its central disc is larger and smooth rather than bristly. The spines on its arms also look more neatly arranged, like the teeth on a comb. The brittle stars can be black or almost any shade of brown, with an attractive pattern sometimes present on the disc. Though often found in aggregations, these tend to be much less dense than those of the common brittle stars, with each individual having something of a "personal space". Mixed groupings of both species are also common.

Black brittle stars obtain their food by catching floating material in a net of mucus or by browsing on algae, organic deposits or carrion. The smaller photograph shows black brittle stars on a bed of maerl (twig-like calcareous seaweed) in Loch Carron. [Up to 25 cm across]

## Sand brittle star  -  *Ophiura ophiura*

Normally found on sand or muddy sand, this species has a relatively large disc and shorter, stiffer arms than many brittle stars. Its arms are much less bristly than the common and black brittle stars. It is typically a drab sandy brown but there may be an attractive

pattern on the central body created by the plates which cover its surface. The sand brittle star can burrow into the sediment or move quite quickly across its surface by using its arms in a "swimming" or "rowing" motion. The animal at the top right of the photograph is a burrowing anemone (see page 45). [Up to 25 cm across but usually much smaller]

## Sand burrowing brittle star  -  *Amphiura brachiata*

As its name suggests, this brittle star lives almost completely buried within sandy seabeds. The whitish or greyish tips of its very long arms protrude from the surface of the sand in order to catch food drifting by. The wavy arms are covered in short spines and it is only these (and the tube feet if visible as in the photograph) that show you are looking at a brittle star and not some type of worm. Aggregations producing a sparse forest of arms are often found, and it is not clear which arms belong to the same individual. In any case, many brittle stars will only have one arm protruding while the others act as anchors. [Up to 40 cm across, but this measurement is very misleading. Usually, only a few cm of an arm or two are visible]

Single arm emerging from sand

# Common (or edible) sea urchin - *Echinus esculentus*

Urchin with tube feet extended

Close-up of urchin, showing tube feet, spines and pedicellariae

## Common (or edible) sea urchin - *Echinus esculentus*

Sea urchins grazing at the bottom of a gully lined with soft corals

The skeleton (also known as a test) of this impressive animal is very rounded and is usually bright red, though the numerous white spine attachment points tend to make it appear pink. Some individuals have a fetching purple hue. The abundant spines are strong, but quite short and thin relative to the overall body size in comparison to other urchins. The bottom photograph on the opposite page is an extreme close-up of an urchin's surface and it shows how the features are very similar to those of a starfish (see page 143), although with different proportions. The spines have the same basic form and the tube feet (top left and lower edge of picture) are almost identical, though of course longer in order to reach out beyond the spines when help with anchoring or movement is required. The pincer-like pedicellariae for removing "free-loaders" have long stems and are particularly noticeable. Without them, the slow-moving urchin would have even more trouble with accumulated debris and unwanted guests than would the relatively (!) athletic starfish. Urchins are powerful and omnivorous grazers, eating animals such as barnacles in addition to algae, and are capable of leaving virtually bare swathes across a rock face. They are abundant in many rocky areas (such as St Abbs, above) and can therefore form an important component of the ecology. Rock-dwelling urchins such as *Echinus* have a feeding mechanism known as Aristotle's lantern (it was he who first described it), which consists of a complex structure of plates and muscles that supports five chisel-like teeth used for scraping food from surfaces. This species is found all around Britain except for the eastern end of the Channel but, in some areas, it has suffered badly from the souvenir trade. [Up to 20 cm across]

## Shore sea urchin - *Psammechinus miliaris*

This urchin is much smaller than the common sea urchin but its spines are longer in relation to its body size, giving it a very spiky appearance. Overall colour is pale green and the spines have fetching purplish tips. As its name suggests, it lives on the shore and in very shallow water. It is often decorated and partly camouflaged by seaweed, shells and other debris trapped among the spines. Like the common sea urchin, this species is an omnivorous grazer. [Up to 6 cm across]

## Common heart urchin (or sea potato) - *Echinocardium cordatum*

Though very abundant, heart urchins are seldom seen because they burrow into a sandy seabed and spend most of their time 10 to 15 cm beneath its surface. The unusual individual shown here was found crawling across the surface of the sand. Unlike the common sea urchin, the test (skeleton) is not round but oval, a shape better suited to the burrowing lifestyle. It also means there is a front and back end. Dense yellow/gold spines cover the test and all point backwards, giving the animal a furry appearance. The spines are used for burrowing, especially the ones shaped like spatulas on the under-surface. Heart urchins construct a channel that runs up to the surface of the sand where it forms a small but noticeable depression. Special, highly elongated tube feet stretch up the channel and are used for respiration and for collecting the deposited particles on which the urchin feeds. Unlike urchins that are crunching grazers, heart urchins possess no Aristotle's lantern. A type of small bivalve mollusc is often found living in association with this species. [Up to 10 cm long]

# Cotton-spinner - *Holothuria forskali*

This large sausage-shaped sea cucumber, found off south west and west Britain, is typically found crawling slowly over exposed rocks. The overall colour is usually black, but the yellow or pale brown on its underside may sometimes spread up over the rest of the body. Most of the body is covered with conical protuberances, except for the flatter underside which bears the tube feet used for locomotion. These features are reminders that you are looking at a relative of the starfish, rather than an exceptionally well fed and prickly slug! The cotton-spinner has short tentacles, rather than the long feathery ones of suspension-feeding sea cucumbers (page 164 and page 165, top), and consumes silty deposits from the sea bed. Having extracted the nutritious organic component, it leaves distinctive trails of undigested material that look like strings of large sandy beads. The name

Defences activated

cotton-spinner comes from the animal's habit of producing long white threads from its rear end if molested (see smaller photograph). The threads are part of its internal organs and are extremely sticky, serving to confuse or entangle the attacker. [Up to 25 cm long]

# Brown sea cucumber - *Aslia lefevrei*

The brown, leathery gherkin-shaped body of this animal is generally hidden in a rock crevice, but its large and highly branched tentacles extend out into open water. The tentacles are dark brown with some white edging often present. Mucus on the tentacles collects suspended matter, and each tentacle is in turn rolled up and inserted into

the central mouth so that the food can be collected (see arm at "five o'clock" position), before it is then re-extended. It is very difficult to watch this process without visualising a child gradually sucking jam from their sticky fingers.

This species can be abundant in some locations in the south west and north west of Britain. The cucumber in the photograph is surrounded by feather stars (page 166) and daisy anemones (page 39). [Tentacles up to 10 cm long]

# Gravel sea cucumber - *Neopentadactyla mixta*

This sea cucumber has feathery white feeding tentacles which are extended above the gravel seabed in which it lives. The tentacles are attractively decorated with brown flecks which can be so dense that the overall colour becomes brown. There may also be striking brown and white patterns around the mouth. A small portion of the long, tapering body may be visible but the majority of

its length is buried and hidden from view. If disturbed, the tentacles can be rapidly withdrawn, though individuals seem to vary greatly in their

sensitivity. Like so many animals that rely on suspended food, they like areas with good water movement. [Tentacles up to 15 cm long]

## Psolus phantapus

The bright orange patches on the creamy coloured tentacles of this sea cucumber species give it a very distinctive appearance. There are also orange or pink spots on the pale body. It is only found in the north of Britain and, even there, is not very widespread. This photograph was taken on a mud slope in Loch Duich where a large number of

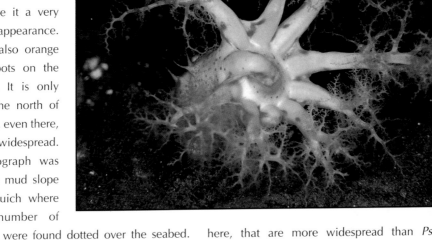

individuals were found dotted over the seabed. All but the tentacle crowns and the upper parts of their bodies were hidden in the mud. There are several similar sea cucumber species, not listed here, that are more widespread than *Psolus phantapus* but less distinctive and attractive. [Tentacles up to 15 cm long]

## Labidoplax digitata

This creature is a sea cucumber even though it looks like a fat bald worm. It burrows in sandy and muddy seabeds and it is often only a section of the long speckly pink body that can be seen as it breaks surface. There are 12 small tentacles around the mouth at one end, usually hidden in the sediment, that are used to collect small particles of dead

organic material. It is unusual amongst sea cucumbers (and echinoderms in general) in having no conventional tube feet. Found all around the west of Britain. [Up to 30 cm long]

# Feather star - *Antedon bifida*

This animal is common around most of the British coast (except the south east) and can occur in abundance. It has ten feathery arms of variable colour, though often red and white, while the overall pattern can produce a mottled or freckled appearance. On the underside of the small central disc there are twenty-five or so shorter claw-like appendages, called cirri, used for anchoring the feather star to the seabed, to kelp stems or to sponges (as in the photograph). Their grip is surprisingly tenacious, as divers who have found them clinging to equipment will know. Feather stars can swim by sweeping their arms up and down, or crawl slowly on the tips of the arms which are bent right over to hold the body away from the seabed. They spend the vast majority of their time, however, simply anchored in their chosen location where they engage in suspension feeding. The arms and their feathery branches

are equipped with numerous tiny tube feet that catch floating food and flick it into grooves which run down each arm. This food is then transported by the beating action of tiny hairs down to the mouth in the centre of the body. Unlike starfish, urchins and brittle stars, feather stars have their mouth on the top side of their body. When not being used for either feeding or locomotion, the arms can be curled up over the body. Though often found singly or in small groups, feather stars are most noticeable when they form huge aggregations. These are most common in current-swept areas not exposed to heavy surf. A closely related feather star (*Antedon petasus*) is larger, neater looking, less freckly and has a greater number (50 or more) of the short claw-like cirri. [*Antedon bifida* up to 15 cm across; *Antedon petasus* up to 20 cm across]

# Celtic feather star - *Leptometra celtica*

This species of feather star has a rather more elegant overall appearance than *Antedon bifida*. The best distinguishing feature, however, is the presence of very long white cirri (claw-like appendages) on the underside of its small central disc. These are used to cling to the seabed. The feathery arms are coloured in white, pale brown or red and are often banded. Usually regarded as a deep water animal, but is quite common in shallow water (around 15 metres) on the west coast of Scotland. [Arms up to 12 cm long]

# Chapter 9

# SEA SQUIRTS

## Unlikely relatives

The sea squirts are a most deceptive group of animals. By living sedentary lives, and feeding by filtering plankton and other food particles from seawater, they appear similar to more primitive creatures such as the sponges. Amazingly, sea squirts are members of the phylum Chordata, the major animal group that contains such creatures as fish, birds and ourselves. The adult sea squirt gives little indication of this elevated status, but the tiny sea squirt larva resembles a tadpole and possesses a very simplified version of the backbone and nerve chord that are characteristic of its advanced relatives.

## Larval secrets

Sea squirt eggs are released into the sea or brooded by the adult, depending on the species. When the larvae, or tadpoles, first hatch from eggs, they swim up towards the light. This is made possible by a light receptor (primitive eye) and a muscular tail which works well because of the stiffening provided by the rudimentary backbone (known as a notochord). Soon however, the larvae's behaviour changes, and they swim away from the light and down towards the seabed. Here, they attach themselves to a suitable substrate with adhesive pads on their front end, and completely lose their youthful mobility.

The tail is reabsorbed, most of their more sophisticated features such as the notochord disappear, and an adult sea squirt results. Many species form colonies.

## The adult form

The adult body is, in essence, a U-shaped tube surrounded by a tough and leathery tunic (this is why sea squirts are also known as tunicates). There is an efficient filtration and pumping system in the centre of the tube, based on the action of numerous beating cilia (tiny hair-like structures). The tube's ends are clearly visible as two openings or siphons: one for the intake of water and one for its expulsion. If a sea squirt is disturbed it can contract its body and water is squirted from the two siphons (hence the name). The body contains an intestine for processing the filtered material and a strange blood circulation system that is unique to sea squirts. Blood is pumped one way round the body for several seconds and the flow is then reversed for an equivalent length of time. Sea squirts are preyed upon by a variety of animals. Sea slugs, in particular, are often seen munching through the colonies. Some species protect themselves by having a highly acidic body wall which renders them unpalatable.

## *Ciona intestinalis*

This widespread and abundant species is the archetypal sea squirt. It is tall, slim and cylindrical in shape but some individuals may be partially contracted and look quite squat. Its translucent tunic, through which the internal organs are usually visible, may be creamy white, pale yellowish green or pale orange-brown. The water intake siphon is at the top of the body with the outflow siphon just off to one side. Both siphons have a distinctive yellow rim and there are tiny red spots between each lobe of the rim that may be seen on close inspection. *Ciona* is fast growing and will rapidly take over freshly available habitats such as marina pilings and

*Ciona* sea squirts with plumose anemone, feather stars and sea urchin

chains. It can form extremely dense aggregations, of up to 5000 squirts per square metre, but the individuals are not fused in any way so it is known as a solitary rather than colonial species. In natural and settled habitats, it is often found in small bunches or in ones and twos. When attempts are made to cultivate shellfish in disused dock basins,

*Ciona* is a serious pest. As highly efficient filter feeders, each pumping up to 3 litres of water an hour and removing particles as small as a thousandth of a millimetre, the sea squirts tend to grab the lion's share of the food as well as the space. [Up to 15 cm tall]

# Light-bulb sea squirt - *Clavelina lepadiformis*

These attractive sea squirts live in bunches that may contain a few or dozens of individuals. The transparent tunic with its delicate yellow or white markings, and the visible internal organs, give the animal its name. Although a colonial species, individuals are free along most of their length and are joined to each other only at their base. The reddish eggs and developing larvae can sometimes be seen within the body cavity. The larvae are released in the late summer and the individual squirts then regress to leave "buds" which survive through the winter and develop into new squirts in the spring. [Up to 2 cm tall. Clumps up to 15 cm across are quite common]

# Football sea squirt - *Diazona violacea*

An aptly named sea squirt that can form large ball-shaped colonies, although small groups such as the one shown here are also common. While there is superficial similarity to the light-bulb squirt, the football's tunic is less transparent and more milky. Individual members of football colonies are also more closely joined together. Small groups of light-bulb squirts in the top-left and top-right of the picture show how the appearances of the two species differ. The football sea squirt is usually restricted to deep clear water and is encountered much less often than the light-bulb squirt. I have only ever noticed it off the west coast of Scotland. [Colonies up to 40 cm across]

## *Aplidium punctum*

This sea squirt forms close-knit colonies where individuals are barely distinguishable from each other. Each colony appears to have a bulbous head on a thinner stalk, and contains approximately forty or more individuals. Close examination reveals that each individual is marked with a tiny dark orange spot that stands out against the generally whitish head. Several colonies are often bunched close together (as shown here), attached to rocks, stones or seaweed. The stalks of the colonies are fairly pale. This species is common in the south west but not elsewhere. Colonies of a very similar species, *Morchellium argus*, that has a wider distribution around western Britain, are more reddish in colour and have red stalks. [Colonies, including stalk, up to 4 cm long]

## Corella parallelogramma

This solitary species is quite small but is one of the most striking sea squirts, with an almost transparent tunic that is often marked by flecks of bright yellow or red. The intricate mesh-like structure that is responsible for pumping water through the body and filtering out food is clearly visible, as are other internal organs. The body tends to be rather flattened and usually has a squarish or oval outline, a little like a full hot water bottle. [Up to 5 cm tall]

## Ascidiella aspersa

The most striking feature of *Ascidiella aspersa* tends to be that it looks dusty and in need of a good clean. This is because its grey tunic has a rough surface which tends to trap a layer of silt and other detritus. A more reliable identification feature is that the water intake siphon looks crimped and is at the top of the body, while the outflow siphon is positioned about a third of the way down the side of the body. Although classified as a solitary sea squirt, it is usually found in clumps. These clumps may cover a large area of muddy seabed, with the squirts attached to pebbles or shells within the mud. [Up to 10 cm tall]

## Ascidia mentula

*Ascidia mentula* is large and generally red or pink in colour, and this combination sets it apart from most sea squirt species. Its colour may be grey in the poor light of deeper water however. Rather than being attached to the seabed by its base like most sea squirts, it is joined on by a part of one side. The intake siphon is at the squirt's free end and is marked with eight white spots which are particularly obvious on deep red individuals. The outflow siphon is about halfway down the body and may be obscured by detritus and encrusting growth. Individuals are often found grouped together so what look like the two siphons of one squirt are in fact the intake siphons of two individuals whose outflow siphons are hidden. [Up to 15 cm long]

## Phallusia mammillata

The largest British sea squirt and a truly solitary species, it is found in the south and west. Lives attached to stones, but often in muddy areas. It is rather plump in appearance and the milk-white or yellowish tunic is unusually thick for a sea squirt and appears quite stiff. Its body surface is covered with rounded, smooth swellings (hence *mammillata*). The water intake siphon is at the very top of the body, the outlet part-way down. Small anemones sometimes live on this sea squirt, taking the opportunity to get away from bottom silt and receive better access to passing food. [Up to 15 cm tall]

## Gooseberry sea squirt - *Dendrodoa grossularia*

This species is defined as solitary because it can live alone, but it is most likely to be seen in aggregations on the walls of rock gullies, under overhangs or on stones. Such groups result from the settling larvae's gregarious behaviour, rather than from budding. The squirts' usual colour is a cherry or orangey red and individuals are normally very rounded in shape and almost dome-like, though some may appear more upright and cylindrical in form. The two protruding siphons are well separated. This species is readily consumed by predatory sea slugs which can sometimes be found chewing their way hungrily through the aggregations. [Up to 2 cm tall]

## Leathery sea squirt - *Styela clava*

A tall sea squirt whose stalk gives it a distinctive club-like shape, although the stalk itself can be hidden by creatures living nearby. Its blotchy brown surface has a slightly "padded quilt-like" appearance and the two siphons, which can bear broad stripes, are right at its top end. It is found singly or in small groups, the photograph shows a row of squirts surrounded by feather stars (page 166). *Styela clava* is actually a native of the Pacific Ocean and is thought to have been brought to our shores on the hulls of ships. It is common in many sheltered areas on the south coast and on the west coast up to South Wales. I have also found it in marinas in East Anglia. [Up to 12 cm tall]

# Star sea squirt - *Botryllus schlosseri*

Close-up of colony

Colonies of star sea squirts are so closely organised that they bear hardly any resemblance to the standard sea squirt form. A colony resides in a common gelatinous tunic, while groups of three to twelve individuals within the colony each produce one of the characteristic star-shaped patterns that cover its surface. Within these groups, the individuals have separate intake siphons but share a common outflow opening in the centre of the star. The basic tunic is usually a dark colour while the stars are a contrasting yellow. Colonies may appear flat or bulbous in their overall shape and are found

encrusting rocks and seaweed. Reproduction can be sexual or achieved by budding. [Colonies around 10 cm across are common]

# Chapter 10

# FISH

One of the first things that strikes someone snorkelling or diving in British waters for the first time is the large number and variety of fish to be seen. While the classic fish shape is represented by species such as bass, grey mullet and pollack, many of the other fish seen in shallow water have different shapes which reflect their bottom-dwelling existence. Adaptations to this lifestyle can include a flattened and enlarged head, with upward-facing mouth, like sea scorpions, weevers and angler fish. Such fish spend a great deal of time lying stationary on the seabed, relying on camouflage to avoid predators and enable them to ambush their prey. Other species have become highly elongated so they can hide amongst seaweed (pipefish) or slip into the narrowest of crevices (conger eels). Still others have thin plate-like bodies, staying upright to sneak up on their prey (John Dory) or lying on their sides on the sea bed (plaice, sole).

## Fins: their layout and function

Despite the variety in fish body shape, it is quite easy to see that all the various species conform to the same basic plan. A good clue is the fins which, despite unusual appearances or adaptations to different functions, are generally laid out in the same pattern (see below). The tail fin provides propulsion and acts as a rudder, while the dorsal and anal fins help with stability by preventing body roll and also act as pivots when the fish is turning. They are known as the

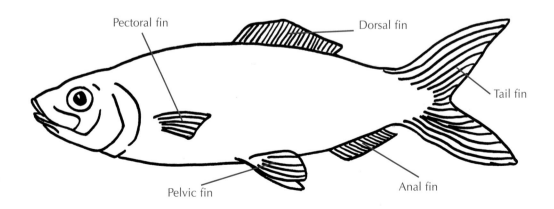

Pectoral fin    Dorsal fin

Tail fin

Pelvic fin    Anal fin

unpaired fins though there may be one, two or even three dorsal fins. The paired fins, pectoral and pelvic, correspond (as their names imply) to the front and hind limbs of land-living vertebrate animals such as ourselves. Pectoral fins are used to help with all sorts of manoeuvres such as turning, braking, rising and falling. The pelvic fins vary considerably in their position from one species to another; they tend to help the pectorals with manoeuvering and maintaining stability. In addition to these basic functions, fins may be used for catching food, repelling predators, mating, courtship display and assisting with camouflage.

## Varied approaches to breeding

Many open sea fish take virtually no care of their young and adopt a "squirt and hope" strategy. A female and male shed vast numbers of eggs and sperm into the water near each other, and seem to make little effort to ensure that fertilisation occurs. Parental attention thereafter is non-existent, and the developing embryos and fish larvae are left entirely to their own devices amongst the plankton in open water. It's not that the parents "don't care", it's simply that they put their energy and resources into quantity rather than quality. Such resources can be substantial, as demonstrated by the weakened state of many fish after breeding. In some species that use this strategy, adults die immediately after their one and only spawning. Many of the shallow water fish familiar to divers use an alternative approach to "squirt and hope". They produce far fewer eggs and make much more strenuous efforts to ensure fertilisation and the survival of the resulting young. It seems that a strategy suited to the open sea is less successful in coastal waters where predators are more numerous and physical conditions are harsher. Abandoned eggs and larvae could easily be washed into less suitable

habitats such as estuaries or deeper water. Interestingly, it is very often the male of common coastal species that takes on the main burden of parenthood. Their nest-building and egg-guarding activities make an interesting spectacle for the observant diver.

## Skeletons of bone or cartilage

The major division in the fish world is that between those with skeletons made entirely from cartilage (sharks and rays) and those with bony skeletons (all the rest). The cartilaginous fish have other characteristic features, such as exposed gill slits and skin covered with tooth-like scales. Their fins are much thicker and more fleshy than those of bony fish, and may also be used slightly differently. The pectoral fins are usually large and, because a buoyancy organ is lacking, act as hydroplanes to provide lift for swimming. Rays have taken this to the extreme and have huge pectoral fins used as wings. Despite these differences, however, the sharks and rays share the same basic fin layout already described. The bony fish have complex and hardened skeletons, similar to those of other vertebrates like ourselves, and their thinner fins are supported by fin rays. They are far more numerous than the cartilaginous fish, with over twenty thousand species versus seven hundred or so. An important characteristic of bony fish is their more sophisticated buoyancy control system, that uses an adjustable gas-filled organ called a swimbladder. By adding or removing gas from the swimbladder, in a similar way to a diver using a buoyancy compensator, neutral buoyancy can be achieved so that energy is concentrated solely on forward motion. However, many of the bony fish species that live on the seabed, such as blennies and flatfish for example, do not actually need this facility and have lost their swimbladders.

# Lesser spotted dogfish - *Scyliorhinus canicula*

Dogfish are in essence small sharks, and this species is much the most common fish of this type encountered by divers around Britain. It has shark-like characteristics such as a mouth positioned on the underside of the head, and obvious gill slits just in front of the hydroplane-like pectoral fins. The dorsal fins are small, rounded and positioned well back on the body, however, and thus bear little resemblance to those of the larger sharks. The body is a greyish brown in colour with numerous dark spots, and a white belly. Tooth-like scales that cover the dogfish have spines that point backwards. The skin, once used as sandpaper, feels quite smooth if stroked from nose to tail and very rough in the opposite direction. Dogfish are often seen "snoozing" on the seabed during the day, sometimes in pairs (opposite page, top photograph) or even in groups. They hunt at night, feeding on crabs, whelks and bottom-living fish such as gobies, dabs and gurnards. Dogfish seem to rely heavily on their sense of smell when hunting and may slavishly follow a scent trail, even when their prey has turned and swum right back past them. They can also detect faint electrical fields produced by the muscles of hidden prey. After mating in the autumn, the female comes inshore during the winter or spring to lay her distinctive pale brown egg capsules, known as "mermaids' purses". These have long tendrils on the corners and, as they are laid, the mother fish will swim round and round a clump of seaweed or similar anchorage, so that they become well attached (opposite page, bottom photograph). Each capsule contains a single embryo and a miniature dogfish emerges after nine months or so. [Fish up to 80 cm long, egg cases are about 7 cm long]

## Lesser spotted dogfish - *Scyliorhinus canicula*

A "snoozing" pair

Egg cases

# Thornback ray - *Raja clavata*

The thornback is the most commonly encountered ray around Britain, being found in relatively deep water and also in very shallow bays and estuaries where this one was photographed. It is usually a blotchy brown or grey and, as the name suggests, bears an array of large thorn-like projections on its back and tail. Some "thorns" have an obvious plate-like base. Rays and skates belong to the same group of fish as sharks and dogfish and, similarly, have a skeleton made of cartilage rather than hard bone. With their flat diamond-shaped bodies, rays can be thought of as "squashed sharks". The greatly enlarged pectoral fins form the "wings" which give them a wonderfully graceful flying motion when swimming. Like most rays, the thornback spends much of its time lying motionless on the seabed where its body shape, along with the habit of covering itself in sand, makes it very difficult to spot. Fish usually take in water for breathing through their mouths, but rays can use the breathing holes (spiracles) behind the eyes on top of their head; they thus avoid taking in too much sand. Like the dogfish, the thornback ray lays its eggs as "mermaid's purses" but these are black rather than brown and lack tendrils. It feeds on a variety of bottom-living animals, especially crabs and shrimps. The closely related common skate (*Raja batis*) has been fished to virtual extinction around most of Britain. Thornback ray populations now seem to be declining too. [Thornback up to 1 m long, skate can be over 2 m long]

# Conger eel - *Conger conger*

The Latin name is uniquely memorable and its owner is pretty unforgettable too. It is a highly elongated fish with a powerful snake-like body, grey-brown to grey-blue in colour with a paler underside. There are no scales and its skin is smooth. The dorsal, tail and anal fins are merged to form a single fringe that runs from just behind the head, right round the pointed tail, to underneath the belly. Congers hide in rocky holes and crevices however, so it is usually only the head that is seen, with its large mouth and distinctive snout bearing a pair of tubular nostrils. Shipwrecks, with all their nooks and crannies, are popular residences. Congers are formidable predators and will slip out of their lair at night to hunt fish, including smaller congers, and large crustaceans such as crabs and lobsters. The latter are seized and may be battered against rocks before being swallowed. Surprisingly, this doesn't seem to stop lobsters and prawns (see page 99) often sharing the crevices that congers use as home. Congers do not breed in our coastal waters but travel vast distances to spawn in the deep mid-Atlantic. Their bodies change as they approach the breeding grounds with teeth falling out, gut degenerating and the gonads becoming so greatly enlarged that they make up a third of body weight. They die after spawning and their larvae drift back into coastal waters and then turn into young eels. Congers have incredibly strong jaws and a reputation for ferocity but remain docile underwater unless provoked, so anglers have more to fear than divers. [Up to 2 m long and occasionally even larger]

## Eel - *Anguilla anguilla*

A slender fish with an amazing life story, it looks similar to the conger but is usually much smaller. As in the conger, the dorsal fin merges with the tail and anal fins to form a single fringe. This starts well behind the pectoral fins, while in the conger it starts very close to the pectorals. The face also appears different because an eel's lower jaw is more prominent than the upper, while a conger's jaws are of equal length or the upper is slightly longer. The eel spends most of its life in rivers and estuaries feeding and growing. Here, it has a green or brown back with a pale yellowish belly and is known as a yellow eel. As it becomes mature, the sides darken to almost black, the belly turns silver and it is described as a silver eel. Silver eels stop eating and go on a long journey down their rivers, through coastal waters and out into the deep Atlantic (mainly the Sargasso Sea) where they spawn. The adults die and the eggs hatch into planktonic leaf-shaped larvae which drift back on the Gulf Stream into European waters and develop into young eels (called elvers). These swim up rivers where they then become yellow eels and the full cycle is complete. [Males up to 50 cm long, females up to 1 m. Most eels seen are much smaller]

## Sprat - *Sprattus sprattus*

The sprat belongs to the silvery shoaling herring family. Other members include the herring itself, the pilchard (called sardine when young) and the anchovy. Common features include a slender body, a single short dorsal fin and a forked tail. Their shape is perfect for rapid swimming in open water and their colouration provides optimum camouflage as it makes them hard to pick out when viewed from any angle. The different species are extremely difficult to identify underwater, as all that is seen is a rapidly-moving mass of silver. A shoal of these fish swirling near the surface is one of the most fabulous underwater sights. The sparkling, swooping maelstrom is usually accompanied by predatory fish darting up from below and sea birds diving in from above to take their share. After a shoal has been subject to such an attack, the water is filled with detached scales looking like tiny scraps of silver paper. The shoal in these pictures consisted mainly of sprat, but there were a few young herring too; identification being based on close examination of fin positions on fish from the whole roll of film. Such mixed shoals of fish are known as "whitebait". The photographs were taken in only 1 metre of water, and within 5 metres of the shore, on the North Sea coast of Scotland. The shoal had been trapped in a rocky inlet by a gang of young saithe (see page 190). Sprat and all members of the herring family feed on small planktonic animals which they sieve from the water as they swim along. In turn, they are an important food source for many large fish, seals and man. The European herring fishery has been of huge historic importance with many coastal towns growing up where the fish could be easily caught and landed. [Sprat up to 15 cm and herring up to 40 cm long, but it is much smaller fish that are usually seen near the coast]

## Sprat  -  *Sprattus sprattus*

Dense shoal of young sprat, with a few herring (both photographs)

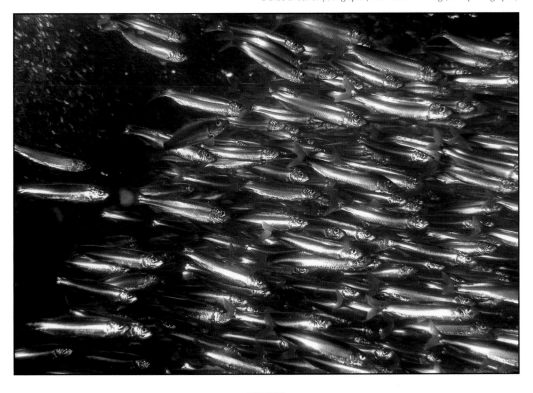

## Connemara clingfish - *Lepadogaster candollei*

Four species of clingfish can be seen around Britain, living mainly in stony areas and within rocky crevices. Common features include their small size, a flattened head roughly triangular in shape and a single dorsal fin close to the tail. They get their name from the strong sucker formed by the merging of the pelvic fins beneath the body, just behind the head. The Connemara clingfish has a long flattened snout, that looks like a duck's bill. General colouration can vary from green to brown or red while large individuals have obvious red spots at the base of the dorsal fin (see photograph). The Cornish sucker or shore clingfish (*Lepadogaster lepadogaster*) has a similar shape and duck-bill snout, but has two large and distinctive blue spots on the top of its head just behind the eyes. The Cornish sucker's dorsal fin is joined to its tail fin while that of the Connemara clingfish is separate. [Both species up to 8 cm long]

## Two-spotted clingfish - *Diplecogaster bimaculata*

The two-spotted clingfish and the very similar small-headed clingfish (*Apletodon dentatus*) share the basic clingfish features with the species described above. Their heads are not quite as flattened, however, and they have much shorter snouts without the duck-bill shape. In both species, there is a short dorsal fin close to, but not joining, the tail. The male two-spotted clingfish has a distinctive purplish spot, with pale edging, on either side of its body just behind the pectoral fin (see photograph). Otherwise, it is virtually impossible to tell apart from the small-headed clingfish underwater. The general colour of both species is very variable. [Both species up to 5 cm long]

# Angler fish - *Lophius piscatorius*

This very unusual fish, gastronomically known as a monkfish, is superbly adapted to its habitat and lifestyle so, considering its potential size, it can be surprisingly difficult to spot. The whole body is flattened, particularly the enormous broad head, and the tail appears small by comparison. Overall body colour is usually brown or greenish-brown with a white underside. Lying on the bottom, its mottled pattern gives good camouflage and the outline is further broken up by the fringe of small flaps of skin round the base of the head. The angler's name, of course, stems from its cunning means of attracting food. The foremost spiny ray of its dorsal fin is separate from the rest of the fin and serves as a "fishing rod". This "rod" can be moved around and the fleshy tip acts as a lure, inviting inquisitive creatures perilously close to the huge upturned mouth. The prey is then engulfed, a process aided by the inrush of water as the angler opens its jaws. Large inward-curving teeth make escape impossible. All sorts of bottom-living fish (including flatfish, gurnards, rays and conger eels) and other animals are eaten, even diving birds. The angler fish spawns in very deep water, laying its eggs in sheets which can form huge rafts up to 10 metres long and have occasionally been mistaken for sea monsters. A sheet typically contains around a million eggs. Hatchlings live freely in open water until they are around 8 cm long, and then take up life on the seabed. Extra-long fins help keep the youngsters afloat, but these have receded by the time the fish come to settle. The angler shown here was found on a ship wreck off Sunderland, the orange in the foreground is one of its rusty plates. [Up to 2 m long but it is much smaller individuals that are usually seen]

## Cod - *Gadus morhua*

Cod in the National Marine Aquarium at Plymouth

The typical cod characteristics are a sensory chin barbel used in the search for food and a distinctive outline created by three closely positioned dorsal fins and two anal fins. Several closely related fish share some or all of these features. Although it is the best known member of this family, the cod itself is generally encountered much less frequently underwater than other family members such as pollack, saithe, bib and ling. Adult cod are more heavily built than those other fish and are also distinguished by the very pale, curved lateral line which is surprisingly obvious underwater (see photographs). The background flank colour can be greenish brown through to dirty yellow or even red, and there is usually a striking marbled pattern. Very young cod have an attractive dense speckling (almost chequered) pattern and can be seen darting amongst seaweed in shallow water. Adult cod are often found cruising amongst rocks in a head-down posture (see smaller photograph) but are very difficult to approach and will dive into the cavity beneath a boulder, or disappear completely, at the slightest provocation. This is why I have had to rely on an aquarium

Cod in the wild

photograph for the main picture. Female cod are renowned for producing several million eggs at a time and theoretical calculations have shown how quickly the Atlantic Ocean would become solid cod if all the eggs were to survive! They don't of course and, ironically, populations of cod have now been so seriously depleted by overfishing in most parts of its range that it is classified as a vulnerable species. Its shy nature and habit of moving into deeper water in the summer (the opposite of many fish) also contribute to it being seen fairly infrequently. [Up to 1.5 m long]

# Ling - *Molva molva*

This long, slim fish is a distinctive member of the cod family. It has the sensory chin barbel worn by most family members but lacks the typical three dorsal fins. Instead, the ling has one short dorsal fin, with a second much longer one behind. The overall colour is

generally a marbled greenish brown; and the dorsal fins have an attractive pale edging which is most obvious when the fish is swimming (see smaller photograph). Youngsters are sometimes decorated with pale purplish iridescent lines. Ling are usually found peering out from rocky holes and crevices; or resting on the seabed just outside their hiding place (main photograph).

They will often sit facing towards it and, if disturbed, will dart back in and watch developments from the safety of their lair. Ling are most commonly seen around Scotland and the far south west. They can be a frequent sighting on wrecks in deep water. [Up to 2 m long. The largest fish normally reside in very deep water below 100 m]

## Pollack - *Pollachius pollachius*

Adult

Seen either singly or in shoals, the pollack is a very common fish in British waters. In many areas, it will be seen on every dive over shallow rocky ground in the summer months. The pollack is a member of the cod family and conforms to their typical pattern of three dorsal and two anal fins, though there is no chin barbel. Adults (main photograph, this page) are generally dark green along the back and more silvery on the sides and belly. The lateral line is usually obvious and takes a marked upward curve by the pectoral fins, in contrast to the straighter lateral line of the very similar saithe (page 190). Juveniles, which can often be seen very close to the shore, are more darkly coloured in green or brown and some may even be a fetching crimson and gold (smaller photograph, this page). With only a little patience, adult pollack can be watched feeding on lesser sand eels (page 201). Hunting individually or in small groups, they will lurk close to the sea bed, gazing watchfully at the sand eel shoal swirling above them (top photograph, opposite page). Suddenly darting up through the shoal, they will grab any unwary fish before returning to near the

Juvenile

bottom and waiting for the shoal to re-group. Juveniles can be seen using an identical technique on groups of mysid shrimps or two-spot gobies (page 218). The bottom photograph on the opposite page shows a pollack with a lamprey attached. Lampreys are primitive jawless fish that feed by attaching themselves to living fish with their mouths, rasping through the host's skin and then sucking their blood. The damage done to the pollack's skin is clear to see. [Pollack are usually up to around 50 cm long, larger fish sometimes seen near wrecks. Juvenile shown above is about 8 cm]

## Pollack - *Pollachius pollachius*

Pair of pollack hunting sand eels

Pollack with lamprey attached. The lamprey is about 25 cm long

# Saithe (coley or coalfish) - *Pollachius virens*

Saithe hunting in a shoal of young sprat

The saithe is a close relative of the pollack and the two can be very hard to distinguish, particularly if they are flashing by in hot pursuit of their prey. The saithe, which is relatively more common in the north of Britain, has jaws of approximately equal length in contrast to the jutting lower jaw of the pollack. The other most noticeable difference is the lateral line which, in the saithe, is approximately straight with a much more gentle curve over the pectoral fin than in the pollack. The saithe in the photograph was, along with colleagues, terrorising a shoal of young sprat (page 183) trapped in a rocky inlet. The saithe could be seen plunging into the shoal and emerging with their struggling prey briefly visible in their mouths before being gulped down. [Up to 1.3 m long, but it is much smaller fish that are usually seen]

## Bib - *Trisopterus luscus*

The bib is another common member of the cod family. Its body has quite a deep shape and is coppery coloured with an attractive banding that is usually, but not always, visible. There is a dark spot at the base of each pectoral fin. These features, in combination with a single barbel underneath the chin, should make the bib very easy to distinguish from all fish other than the poor-cod (below). Bib are frequently seen inside and near wrecks in small or large groups. Shoals of very small bib, often found over the sand near wrecks, will approach and even surround divers whilst in search of any small pieces of food that they stir up from the bottom. Bib feed on crustaceans, such as shrimps, and molluscs with older fish eating other fish and squid too. [Up to 50 cm long but usually no more than 30 cm]

## Poor cod - *Trisopterus minutus*

Belonging to the same genus as the bib, the poor cod is a close relative and possesses a very similar appearance. It shares features such as the protruding upper jaw and the long barbel on the lower. The poor cod can be distinguished from the bib by its shallower body shape, lack of banding and generally smaller size. It may be seen individually or in quite large groups. Shoals of small fish seen near wrecks are often a mixture of both bib and poor cod. [Up to 25 cm long]

## John Dory - *Zeus faber*

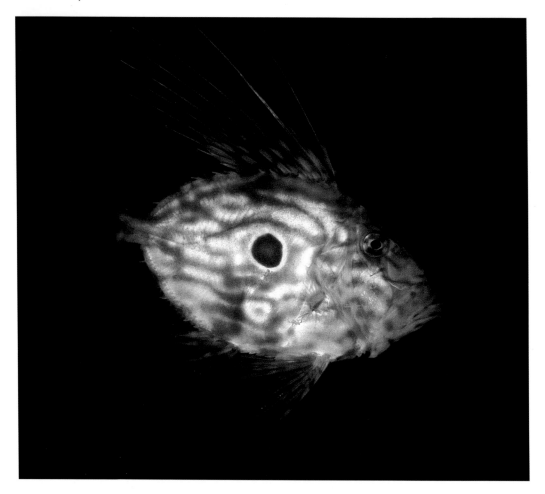

A highly distinctive fish, the John Dory has a body shaped like a flat oval plate on edge. Other notable features are the large head with its mournful expression, the very long dorsal fin rays and a single dark spot in the centre of each flank. The thin body virtually disappears when viewed head-on or tail-on (see photograph opposite), a characteristic used to good effect when approaching unsuspecting prey or avoiding predators. While not a rapid mover, the John Dory shows great manoeuvrability when stalking its prey, swimming while tilted at all sorts of angles and even upside down. At the same time, stripes on its flanks can alternately recede and intensify which, when coupled with the thin outline, makes its approach even harder to spot. Its jaws have a special bone construction which makes them highly protrusible. Once close to its unsuspecting prey, the mouth shoots out to engulf the victim. Prey is usually small fish such as sand-eels, herring and pilchards. In the shallow water where encounters with divers tend to occur, they are often seen hunting the two-spot gobies (page 218) that hover in patches of sea weed. Legend has it that the dark blotches on each flank are St Peter's fingerprints, left when he took a coin from the fish's mouth to pay his tax. [Up to 60 cm long but usually much smaller]

## John Dory - *Zeus faber*

Turned head-on, the slender outline of the John Dory is much harder to see

# Greater pipefish - *Syngnathus acus*

Pipefish look very much like straightened and elongated sea horses, which are in fact their close relatives. Pipefish are like sea horses in having no scales. They have a series of jointed, bone-like rings which encircle the body from just behind the head down to the tail, giving most species a rather rigid, armoured appearance. The small mouth is positioned at the end of a slender snout and is used to suck in the

tiny animals on which pipefish feed. Pipefish may move around by using a snake-like body action or, like sea horses, by rapid fluttering movements of their fins. The characteristic features of *Syngnathus acus* are its rough body with angular cross section, the very long snout taking up more than half the total length of the head and the bump on top of the head behind the eyes.

It is usually found amongst seaweed or eel-grass where its shape and colour provide effective camouflage. The fish species that live in shallow water generally give their eggs good care, but pipefish take this to the extreme. The female lays her eggs into a special brood pouch on the belly of the male, where the young develop until emerging as miniature adults. [Up to 50 cm long]

# Snake pipefish - *Entelurus aequoreus*

The snake pipefish is easily distinguished by its striking colouration of orange-brown with thin but clearly defined pale hoops. There is also a fetching dark stripe running back through the eye. Aside from the colour, it is also rather different in form to the greater pipefish and similar species. The body is much smoother and more rounded in cross section, so it does not appear armoured. There are also no pectoral fins and the tail fin is virtually non-existent (see smaller photograph), so the overall effect is certainly snake-like. Snake pipefish are often found using their tail curled round seaweed as an anchor, while they swing round sucking in their food of tiny floating animals. Rather than having a special brood pouch like that of other pipefish, the male snake

Tail used as anchor

pipefish carries the eggs in a simpler hollow on the outside of its belly. [At up to 60 cm long, this species is our largest pipefish]

# Long-spined sea scorpion - *Taurulus bubalis*

The long-spined sea scorpion, sometimes simply referred to as the sea scorpion, is a common fish of shallow water and surprisingly large individuals can even be found in rockpools. The first part of its name comes from the long sturdy spine pointing backwards from each gill cover. There are also some smaller spines nearby but none are venomous, unlike those of the Mediterranean scorpion fish. A distinctive little barbel is visible at either corner of the mouth. The broad head has bony crests and there are no scales but, instead, bony plates embedded in the skin. The sea scorpion's irregular outline and mottled patterning is only part of its camouflage story, for it has an impressive ability to replicate the colour of its surroundings. It will often stay perfectly still when approached, just swivelling its eyes to assess the intruder. The varied habitat of the shallow waters in which they live give sea scorpions plenty of opportunity to show off their colour mimicry repertoire of pinks (encrusting algae), deep reds and browns (seaweeds) and oranges (sponges). These pages show some good examples of this chameleon-like activity, although the fish in the final photograph is included because it seems to have lost the plot. The claws and legs protruding from the corners of its mouth may be the explanation. In the act of grabbing or attempting to swallow the crab, it has moved from another position and apparently forgotten (or simply not had time) to blend in! The sea scorpion is in fact a voracious predator, creeping up on crustaceans or fish and then lurching forward to take them in a single gulp. Surprisingly large prey can be taken in the wide mouth. Like a number of bottom-living fish, sea scorpions lack a swimbladder to provide buoyancy and this explains their rather ungainly movements. Breeding takes place in the spring and clusters of orange eggs are laid in rock crevices or amongst seaweeds. [Up to 20 cm long]

**Long-spined sea scorpion - *Taurulus bubalis***

Orange to match sponge

Maroon to match seaweed

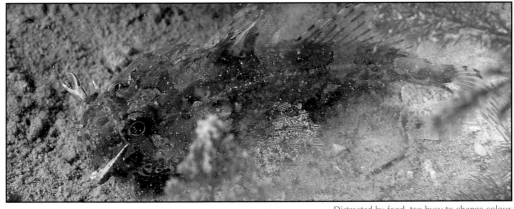

Distracted by food, too busy to change colour

## Short-spined sea scorpion (or bull rout) - *Myoxocephalus scorpius*

This stout fish, which also goes by the fine name of "father lasher", is very similar in appearance to the long-spined sea scorpion (pages 196-197) but it can grow to a larger size. The "short-spined" name refers to the fact that the spines on its gill covers are all fairly short and there is no single long spine as in the other species. The spines are very difficult to see underwater, however, and the best distinguishing feature is that the short-spined sea scorpion has no flap of skin (barbel) at either side of the mouth. This sounds like a trivial feature but is surprisingly easy to spot underwater.

Short-spined sea scorpions can be found on all types of seabed, hard or soft, and appear capable of imitating the colouration of their background without having quite the breadth of repertoire shown by their long-spined relatives. The fish in the photograph had just grabbed a small shore crab whose legs can be seen protruding from the mouth of its nemesis. I had been watching as the sea scorpion eyed up its prey from about 40 cm away and it took the crab with a burst of startling speed. [Up to 30 cm long]

# Lumpsucker - *Cyclopterus lumpus*

This strange fish has the least graceful appearance imaginable. Its stockily built body is rounded and humped, and the head is massive and very wide. It is protected by bony plates which form rows of bumps running along the length of the body. Colouration is bluish, greyish or greenish, the male taking on a reddish belly or flanks in the breeding season. There are two dorsal fins, but the foremost fin becomes overgrown by thick skin with age. The pelvic fins are fused to form a powerful sucker on the underside, just behind the chin, which is used for clinging onto rock surfaces. Lumpsuckers spend most of their time in fairly deep water but, between February and May, pairs meet up in shallow water where the female lays her eggs in a mass on a rocky ledge. She immediately returns to deeper water but the male stays to take care of the eggs

Male with eggs (both photographs)

for the one or two months until they hatch. It is during this time that most lumpsuckers are seen. The devoted father can keep scavenging animals away, but his chief duty may well be to keep the eggs oxygenated. He achieves this by fanning them with his fins or by pushing his head into the mass; the indentations caused by this action can sometimes be spotted. Any eggs that become rotten may also be eaten in order to keep the rest healthy. Egg masses are often laid in very shallow water, sometimes above low water mark, so wave surge could cause a real problem for the attendant male if he lacked the help of his sucker to keep him in position. The two photographs on this page show a male lumpsucker guarding a pale yellow egg mass amongst rocks in a few metres of water in April. [Females up to 60 cm long, males up to 50 cm]

## Pogge (or hooknose) - *Agonus cataphractus*

An odd but unobtrusive fish usually found on sand or mud, the pogge has a head and body completely covered with keeled, bony plates. The underside of the wide but pointed head is covered with a beard-like array of barbels, and a pair of heavy curved spines on the snout gives the impression of an upturned nose. The pectoral fins are large but, behind them, the body tapers away to a very slim tail stem. Overall colour is greyish-brown with darker patches. The pogge seems content to rely on its armour and camouflage for defence; and appears unperturbed when approached. [Up to 20 cm long but usually smaller]

## Grey gurnard - *Eutrigla gurnardus*

Gurnards are another group of fish whose head is armoured with bony plates, but they have an unusual profile created by a very steep forehead. Their pectoral fins are also distinctive, with the foremost three rays separated from the rest of the fin to form "fingers" which probe for food and can "walk" the fish across the seabed. The grey gurnard is mainly a greyish

or reddish brown with numerous small pale blotches and an off-white underside. A dark blotch is often visible on the foremost dorsal fin. Other very similar gurnard species are distinguished by brilliant blue markings on the pectoral fins (tub gurnard, *Trigla lucerna*) or an overall red colour (red gurnard, *Aspitrigla cuculus*). [Up to 45 cm long]

## Lesser sand eel - *Ammodytes tobianus*

Usually seen in dense shoals in sandy areas, particularly where there are also weed-covered rocks. They are very thin, silvery fish with a jutting lower jaw and forked tail fin. Shoals can swim very quickly, however, and all that may be seen is a swirling group of silvery streaks. Some of their time is spent buried in sand and an entire shoal

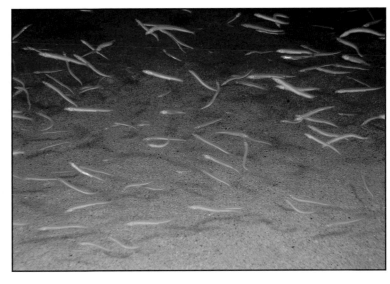

can disappear into the seabed in seconds. Conversely, a hand put down on the sea floor can cause a shoal to erupt into the open, a startling experience for the unwary. Shoals can be watched being followed by predators such as the greater sand eel (below), pollack (pages 188-189) and bass (page 202). They form a major food source for many fish and sea birds. [Up to 20 cm long]

## Greater sand eel - *Hyperoplus lanceolatus*

These fish are very similar in form to lesser sand eels (above) but, in addition to being larger, can appear quite different when seen underwater. They tend to swim in much smaller groups of only a few individuals and move with a far more purposeful and menacing attitude. I have

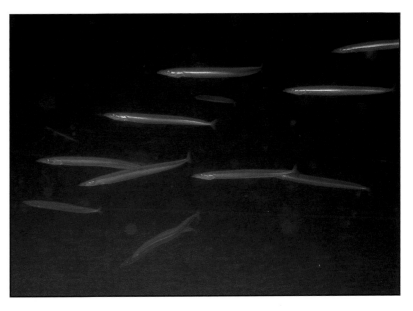

encountered greater sand eels most often when they are hunting lesser sand eels. A dark spot on the snout is a distinguishing feature of the greater sand eel but they usually move too quickly for this to be noticeable other than in photographs. [Up to 35 cm long]

## Bass - *Dicentrarchus labrax*

Bass are free swimmers, normally seen in small shoals in shallow rocky areas. They are more thick-set than fish such as pollack and saithe, and have much larger heads and mouths than grey mullet, but still appear very streamlined. The flanks are bright silver with the back slightly darker. Bass have a distinctly menacing look, and give the entirely accurate impression of being fast and voracious hunters. When found lurking near a wreck or reef, they will usually disappear immediately. A shoal may

occasionally circle a stationary diver at a distance however, with a curious individual or two swooping down to take a closer look. [Up to 80 cm long]

## Lesser weever - *Echiichthys vipera*

The lesser weever is one of the very few venomous fish found in British waters, and it can be quite common in shallow sandy areas. Its head has an extremely deep shape and this, coupled with the upturned mouth, gives it a distinctive and very grumpy appearance. Behind the head, the body slims down and ends in quite a slender tail. Weevers spend most of their time almost completely buried in the sand with often only their eyes uncovered. When disturbed, they swim off surprisingly rapidly. On swimming

off, or when disturbed while resting, the black front dorsal fin stands erect. It is this and spines on the gill covers that can inject poison if the fish is handled or accidentally trodden on. This sting is excruciatingly painful and soaking in hot water is said to break down the toxin and reduce the pain. The greater weever (*Trachinus draco*) is also venomous but is rare in shallow water. [Lesser weever up to 15 cm long, greater weever up to 40 cm]

# Red mullet - *Mullus surmuletus*

The most distinctive features of this attractive fish are the pair of long feelers or barbels on its chin and the steep sloping forehead. The scales on its body are very obvious and the colour varies from yellow-brown to orange red, usually with pretty stripes or patterning. Red mullet can be seen "snuffling" around on sandy or muddy seabeds, using their barbels to feel for small buried animals on which they feed (see photograph). They are common in many sandy bays, often occurring in small groups. If a group is approached too closely, an individual fish raising its front dorsal fin seems to act as a signal for all the mullet to swim off. [Up to 40 cm long but usually much smaller]

# Thick-lipped grey mullet - *Chelon labrosus*

Grey mullet are common but very shy fish. Divers or snorkellers can see them very close to stony beaches, sometimes in shoals, but one often gets only the most fleeting of glimpses as they disappear rapidly when approached. Groups of small individuals are found in rock pools. The grey to silvery body is torpedo-shaped with fairly distinct stripes down the flanks. If not scared off, grey mullet can be watched grazing head-down on the seabed, scraping algae off stones and rocks or sucking up mud to extract any edible matter. The intestine is very long in order to handle this austere diet. There are two other similar species, the thin-lipped and golden grey mullets. [Up to 70 cm long]

# Cuckoo wrasse - *Labrus bimaculatus*

Male

The colourful wrasse are some of the most frequently seen fish in Britain's coastal waters. Individuals of most of the five common species will be seen on many dives in rocky areas, particularly in the summer months. The cuckoo wrasse may not be the most abundant of them, but its magnificent

Female

colouration and unusual behaviour tend to make it the most notable. An inquisitive and territorial male (top photograph) will often swim up to a diver's mask and look them straight in the eye before following them at close quarters, even taking the odd nibble on occasion. Males have a brilliant blue head with further blue markings interspersed with orange or yellow down the flanks. All cuckoo wrasse start life as females. Females are a coral pink with a distinctive row of black and white blotches along the rear of the back (smaller photograph). Some females turn into males later in life, depending on the proportion of the sexes in the local population. Individuals at an intermediate stage between female and male colouration will sometimes be seen. The cuckoo wrasse is usually restricted to slightly deeper water than the other wrasse species, so is seen less often when diving from the shore. [Males up to 35 cm long, females usually smaller]

# Ballan wrasse - *Labrus bergylta*

Adult

The ballan is the largest of our wrasse, and has the appearance of being more heavily-built than the other slimmer species. Colouration is extremely variable, with many shades of brown, grey, green and red being found. There may be strong saddle-type markings, a mottled pattern or a single light stripe running the length of the body. Each of the large scales is usually relatively pale in the middle, and darker round the edge, which can give the whole fish a very spotty appearance. The young ballans, found in very shallow water and amongst seaweed in rock pools, are usually a vibrant emerald green (see smaller photograph). Like its close relative the cuckoo wrasse, the ballan always starts life as a female but some individuals become males later in life, usually after several years of breeding as a female. Unlike the cuckoo however, ballan wrasse show no obvious colour change to mark their change of sex. One can only presume it must be obvious to other ballan wrasse! Most populations have many more females than males. The ballan is abundant in

Juvenile

most rocky areas, from very shallow water down to 20 metres depth or so. It uses its strong front teeth to prise encrusting molluscs or barnacles from the rocks and also has additional teeth in the throat for crushing its food. When accompanied by rock cooks, I have seen it take in mouthfuls of gravel (see pages 206-207). Along with many fish species, the ballan wrasse is seen much less frequently out and about in shallow water during the winter. At this time however, small groups of individuals can often be found hiding in narrow rocky crevices. [Up to 50 cm long]

# Rock cook - *Centrolabrus exoletus*

The rock cook is sometimes the forgotten species in descriptions of the wrasse, but it is abundant in many areas (except in the south east of England) and will often be seen in groups around a reef or piece of wreckage. Broadly similar in appearance to the other small wrasse, rock cooks are usually a pale reddish-brown with blue lines running along the side of the head; in the summer males have additional blue colouring down their back and flanks. The best distinguishing mark, however, is the broad dark band across the tail fin. The most notable feature of rock cook behaviour is their intriguing relationship with ballan wrasse. Rock cooks act as cleaner fish on the larger wrasse and will remove parasites from their flanks. Small groups of rock cooks can sometimes be seen escorting a single ballan,

appearing to take turns in darting forward to have a quick nibble (top photograph, opposite page). Certain locations, such as the boilers on a shallow-water wreck, seem to serve as "cleaning stations" where this behaviour can regularly be observed. In some areas, particularly where patches of gravel intersperse the rocks around which the wrasse congregate, the two species also seem to feed together. A ballan hunting in the gravel for food may be surrounded by its little cohort of rock cooks looking for any scraps that are stirred up (bottom photograph, opposite page). The ballan will sometimes take a mouthful of small stones and spit them out, the rock cooks dashing in to examine material that starts to float away. [Up to 15 cm long]

Rock cook - *Centrolabrus exoletus*

Rock cook cleaning ballan wrasse

Rock cooks feeding with ballan wrasse

# Goldsinny - *Ctenolabrus rupestris*

This small and slim wrasse lacks the colour and pattern variations displayed by most of its relatives, and so it is easier to identify. As the name suggests, the general colouration is a pinky or reddish brown akin to gold. The belly is paler and there may be faint stripes along the flanks. Aside from the colour, a reliable distinguishing feature is the large black spot located on the top side of the tail stem. The goldsinny's overall body shape is slightly different from that of the other wrasse species, being more torpedo-shaped. It swims in the typical manner common to all the wrasse however, usually keeping its body fairly stiff and using a rowing motion of the pectoral fins for propulsion. It can be very common in rocky areas, especially around underwater cliffs or rocky drop-offs, but is less abundant in the shallowest waters of the seaweed zone than the rock cook and corkwing. Goldsinnies will often approach divers quite closely, swimming to and fro in front of them but darting for cover if they make any sudden movements. They seem very inquisitive and I have often noticed them swimming round my head, gazing intently at my air bubbles while I take photographs. When observed closely, the protruding points of their outer row of teeth can be seen. These teeth enable goldsinnies to feed on encrusting organisms, as well as small crustaceans and other bottom-living animals. They act as cleaners to larger fish (in a similar way to the rock cook, pages 206-207) and have been used to remove parasites from caged salmon in fish farms. [Up to 20 cm long]

# Corkwing wrasse - *Crenilabrus melops*

Male with nest

The corkwing is another small wrasse and is very abundant. It can be found in very shallow water, and the young are common in rock pools low down on the shore. The body is quite deep when viewed in profile, but rather slim when seen head-on. Distinguishing features include stripes on the cheeks, a dark blotch in the shape of a comma behind each eye and a dark spot in the middle of the tail stem (the latter can be very difficult to see). The overall colour is variable with females generally a pale brown, and males a darker more greenish brown, with hints of blue or dark red. Breeding males have superb colouration with brilliant blue or green mixed with claret, and very prominent cheek stripes. In the spring and early summer, male corkwings can be watched bustling around the rocks collecting scraps of seaweed in their mouths, which they then ram into a crevice to create a nest. Males invite females in to lay their eggs using a courtship display, and may try their luck with more than one female. Females with eggs can be recognised by the blue egg-laying papilla (protuberance) near

Female with blue egg-laying papilla visible

the anal fin (see smaller photograph). After laying, the female has no more parental involvement but the male, once he has fertilised the eggs and put more seaweed over them, guards the nest. When engaged in building or guarding activities, the normally shy corkwing becomes bold and will attempt to ward off any approach to the nest. On occasion, they seem to swim away from the nest in full view and then return surreptitiously beneath the nearby kelp, as though attempting to mislead the potential predator. The main photograph shows a male making adjustments to his nest. [Up to 25 cm long]

## Tompot blenny - *Parablennius gattorugine*

Though usually small, tompot blennies are among the most charismatic fish seen in British waters. Their distinctive clown-like faces can frequently be seen peering out from crevices in reefs or wrecks, but they can also be found out in the open. Very small tompots are sometimes seen on the shore. The tompot blenny has a large mouth and eyes set high up on the head which, along with the large branched tentacle above each eye, contribute to the comical appearance. A much smaller fringed tentacle is positioned on the nostril beneath each eye. The elongated body is taller than it is broad, with a single dorsal fin that stretches almost back to the tail. The body's overall colour is a reddish or olive brown with several dark bands along its length. Like all blennies, tompots lack the buoyancy of a swimbladder and swim with a clumsy, though surprisingly rapid, wriggling motion. If the same site is dived regularly, a particular tompot may be spotted in the same hole on each visit. If the hole is empty, a short wait can result in the amusing sight of the resident bustling back into its home. Tompots are extremely inquisitive fish and may emerge from their shelter to take a closer look at the visiting diver. The odd individual may allow itself to be gently stroked, even appearing to become agitated when this is stopped. Tompot blennies will sometimes rush from their hiding place to see off other blennies or an intruding velvet swimming crab. They possess a single row of sharp teeth in each jaw and eat a variety of animals from the sea bed, including sea anemones which are unpalatable to most predators. The tompot appears to be absent from the North Sea. [Up to 30 cm long but usually much smaller]

Tompot blenny  -  *Parablennius gattorugine*

## Shanny - *Lipophrys pholis*

The shanny, occasionally known as the common blenny, is a widespread and abundant fish of the shore and shallow water. It is usually seen in rock pools, by snorkellers, or by divers at the beginning or end of a beach dive. As well as hiding under stones or in holes, it can be seen in the open on barnacle covered rocks where its mottled pale brown and green colouring provides excellent camouflage. The shanny can also change colour to match its surroundings. It is very similar in shape to the tompot, but is usually smaller and lacks any head tentacles. It is more timid than the tompot and, when approached, it may carefully watch the viewer for just a few seconds before wriggling into a rock crack or under some seaweed. The two species have similar parenting arrangements, with the male guarding the eggs for a month or more until they hatch. During breeding and nesting, the male shanny's colours darken to almost black while the lips are a contrasting white. Shannies are omnivorous, eating seaweed as well as small animals such as worms and shrimps. They can sometimes be watched attempting to nip off the feeding limbs of barnacles as these sweep out to catch food. A shanny may live for as long as sixteen years. [Up to 15 cm long]

## Montagu's blenny - *Coryphoblennius galerita*

The Montagu's blenny lives in the same rock pool and rocky shore habitat as the shanny and has a similar overall appearance. It is distinguished by a fringed crest between the eyes which is quite different from the prominent pair of head tentacles worn by the tompot blenny. Montagu's blenny also has small pale blue spots on its greeny brown head and body. Like young shannies, it eats the feeding limbs of barnacles which are abundant in the environment where it lives. This species is only found in the south west of Britain and, even there, is seen much less frequently than the shanny or tompot. [Up to 8 cm long]

## Black-face blenny - *Tripterygion delaisi*

Black-face blennies are quite rare but can be seen time and again in particular locations on the south coast. They can be found regularly in a rocky gully near Wembury in South Devon for instance (where this one was photographed) and Portland in Dorset is another favoured spot. They will often rest upside-down, under an overhang. Females are a drab mottled brown while males are more colourful and have distinct black heads in the breeding season. Some of the fins bear an attractive sky-blue edging. Unlike the true blennies which have slippery skin and a single long dorsal fin, this fish has scales and three dorsal fins. [Up to 7 cm long]

## Yarrell's blenny - *Chirolophis ascanii*

This fish is often seen peering out from a rock crevice where, at first glance, it can look like a mournful tompot blenny. When found out in the open, as here on the wreck of the Shuna in the Sound of Mull, it is obviously much longer and more slender than other blennies with head decoration such as the tompot or Montagu's. If examined closely, the face alone is distinctive. A dark ring around each eye extends into a stripe down the cheek; and the head tentacles are tall with branched and very tufty ends. There are further smaller tentacles on the head and the front few spines of the dorsal fin also have tufty tips. This species is more common in the north of Britain. Like the black-face blenny, it is not classified as a true blenny. [Up to 25 cm long]

## Butterfish (or gunnel) - *Pholis gunnellus*

The eel-shaped butterfish, named after its slippery skin, is distinguished by the row of white-edged black spots along the base of its dorsal fin. Not a true blenny, but a close relative. Butterfish are found in crevices or creeping around the base of kelp plants, sometimes lifting their heads, snake-like, to get a better view. Their eggs are laid between December and March, in rock cavities or empty mollusc shells in shallow water. Butterfish are very unusual in that both parents may take turns to guard the eggs (in most blennies and similar fish it is just the male). They curl their bodies around the eggs and prevent them from being scattered. The butterfish is very common around all British coasts. [Up to 25 cm long]

## Wolf-fish - *Anarhichas lupus*

Wolf-fish are creatures of cold northern seas, and Britain is about as far south as they get. They often lurk at depths of between 100 and 300 metres but in some locations, such as on the east coast of Scotland, they can be found in as little as 10 metres of water. Here, they will usually be encountered peering out from the shelter of a cave or crevice and that fierce-looking face with prominent fang-like teeth is unmistakable. Their shape, with a large head and long tapering body with elongated dorsal fin is similar to that of an enormous blenny. Wolf-fish prey includes armoured animals such as urchins, crabs and whelks, which are crunched up with the help of strong grinding teeth on either side of the jaws and powerful cheek muscles. New teeth grow up from behind to replace the worn set every year. The same wolf-fish individuals can be seen in particular caves summer after summer, but they are assumed to move into deeper water in the winter. The female lays her eggs in the winter, producing large ball-like clumps of several thousand yellowish eggs on the sea bed. After two months these hatch into larval fish which stay on the bottom while they use up their yolk reserves, but then spend some time floating with the plankton. They finally settle back on the seabed by the following autumn. [Up to 1.2 m long]

## Viviparous blenny - *Zoarces viviparus*

As the term "viviparous" in its name indicates, this fish is remarkable because it bears live young, up to 300 at a time. The eggs, instead of being shed or laid as in the majority of fish, develop within the female's body during the 3 to 4 months after mating. The young are born in the winter, about 4 cm long. It is a long slender fish, with the dorsal, tail and anal fin

merged to form a single fringe. There is a distinctive notch in the top of this fringe just in front of the tail. It can be distinguished from other slender blenny-like fish because it has no obvious spots (as in the butterfish) or head tentacles (as in the Yarrell's blenny). The viviparous blenny, also known as the eelpout, is found around Scotland and right down the east coast of England. This photograph was taken in a marina in East Anglia. [Up to 50 cm long, usually 30 cm or less]

## Black goby - *Gobius niger*

Gobies are very abundant small fish, occasionally confused with blennies. Unlike blennies which tend to move with a wriggle, gobies have swimbladders and swim with a more graceful darting movement. They also possess two dorsal fins to the blennies' one. The black goby, common on sea beds of sand and mud, is larger and stouter than most gobies. Not really black, it is found in

various shades of brown with darker blotches. There is a black mark at the front corner of both dorsal fins and the foremost fin is quite triangular in shape. Gobies have similar breeding habits to blennies, with the male taking on egg-guarding duties. [Up to 17 cm long]

# Rock goby - *Gobius paganellus*

Goby eating a prawn

Another fairly stout goby, this species is found on rocky ground as the name implies. Common in the south and west, but apparently absent from the east coast, it is found in rock pools on the shore, and divers will often see it peering out from a crevice or hole. The front dorsal fin has a pale band along its top edge, which can be red or orange in adult males. A further distinguishing feature is the tiny branched tentacle by each nostril, though this is usually only seen when close-up photographs are examined after a dive. The fish in this photograph has just swallowed a surprisingly large prawn, and its tail can be seen protruding from the goby's mouth. [Up to 12 cm long]

# Painted goby - *Pomatoschistus pictus*

Gobies scavenging around a feeding crab

Several types of slim fawn gobies are seen darting across sandy seabeds. The painted goby can be recognised by its dorsal fins that are decorated by one or two rows of black spots. Reddish bands above the spots are especially developed in breeding males. The photograph shows a number of painted gobies darting expectantly around a feeding harbour crab (page 80-81), hoping for any scraps. Divers disturbing the sand will also get the same attention because they may uncover small worms or shrimps. Two closely related species, the common goby (*P. microps*) and the sand goby (*P. minutus*) tend to live in areas with finer sand or mud. They have no obvious spots on their dorsal fins but are very difficult to tell apart from each other. [All three *Pomatoschistus* species are rarely more than 6 cm long]

# Two-spot goby - *Gobiusculus flavescens*

Two-spot gobies do not rest on the seabed for much of the time like other gobies, but dart continually around in the water a few inches above the bottom, often in patches of seaweed. This habit, as much as its markings, makes the species easy to identify. General colouration is reddish brown, with a paler underside and pretty pale blue markings along the sides of the body. There is a conspicuous black spot at the base of the tail fin, and males have another dark spot on their sides just behind the pectoral fin, hence the name. In their breeding season during the spring and early summer, males develop beautifully iridescent blue lines on their dorsal fins (see bottom photograph). Females usually lay their eggs around the base of kelp plants and the males then guard them until they hatch. Two-spot gobies are usually found in small groups and these groups can sometimes be watched being tracked by predators such as young pollack (pages 188-189) or a John Dory (pages 192-193). The gobies eat floating food such as larval animals or tiny planktonic shrimps. [Up to 6 cm long]

Male goby, with obvious spot behind the pectoral fin. Many are less reddish than this one

Breeding male with iridescent blue lines on its dorsal fins

# Leopard-spotted goby - *Thorogobius ephippiatus*

The attractive colouration of this splendid little fish makes it easier to identify than any of the other gobies. The overall body colour is a mauve-grey or fawn, and there are numerous dark brown or brick-red blotches all over the body and head. A fetching pale blue edging to the dorsal fins is sometimes visible. When studied closely, the outlines of the large diamond-shaped scales are also quite noticeable. Far from taking pride in their appearance, leopard-spotted gobies are extremely shy fish, disappearing into rocky crevices or the cavities beneath boulders at the first sign of attention. Escape is made even quicker by their tendency, while resting on the seabed, to face towards their refuge. This attitude contrasts sharply with that of many other small fish, who seem keen to watch the world go by. Despite being so shy, leopard-spotted gobies are a frequent sight when diving in rocky areas, particularly if a little sand or silt is present around the crevices. Before diving in such areas was commonplace, it was assumed to be a very rare species because so few were caught in trawls. It is fairly widespread but has not been reported on the east coast south of St. Abbs. [Up to 12 cm long]

# Dragonet - *Callionymus lyra*

A slender fish seen darting away on a sandy seabed may well be a dragonet, but with this behaviour and the prominent eyes on top of the head, small specimens could be confused with gobies. The dragonet, however, has a much broader and nearly triangular head when seen from above. The snout is also much longer and incorporates a jutting lower jaw. Females and juvenile males are usually a pale, blotchy brown, sometimes with attractive mottling or patterns (top photograph). They are also capable of blending in perfectly with a coarse sand or gravel seabed. The adult male is impressively coloured in hues of blue and yellow (bottom photograph) but is unfortunately a rare sight. Courtship apparently consists of the male performing an elaborate display, darting around in front of a female while spreading his brightly coloured fins and even

Female or juvenile male

Adult male

pulling a strange face. Once the female is suitably impressed, they swim up towards the surface together and shed eggs and sperm into the water, their anal fins being positioned in such a way as to keep these together long enough for fertilisation to occur. Males are thought to only breed once in a lifetime. Dragonets feed on small animals in the sand such as worms and crustaceans. Individual fish react differently when encountered, some disappearing rapidly while others seem content to be approached and photographed. [Females up to 20 cm long, males up to 30 cm]

# Plaice - *Pleuronectes platessa*

A common flatfish, frequently found on sandy and muddy seabeds, or on sand patches in rocky areas. They may be seen at any depth between the shore and very deep water. Plaice are easily distinguished from relatives such as flounder and dab by the characteristic orange spots scattered over the upper side of their body. The background colour is usually grey-brown but this can change to blend in with the seabed; the underside is a pearly white. Flatfish such as plaice are of course actually lying on their sides. Newly hatched from the floating egg, tiny flatfish look like conventional fish with the body positioned vertically in the water and an eye on either side. As they develop, still in open water, the body prepares itself for the bottom-living life. By the time the young fish have settled on the seabed, one eye has moved over to join the other eye on the same side of the body, thus producing the typically twisted facial expression of all flatfish. Plaice are "right-eyed" in that the eyes both end up on what was originally the fish's right side. Female plaice lay up to half a million eggs at a time. Mating is not intimate as eggs and sperm are simply released into the water, but the female takes care to release her buoyant eggs beneath the male so they float up through his sperm to maximise fertilisation. Plaice are usually seen only when stationary, but prey on animals such as cockles, shrimps, worms and brittle stars while cruising over the seabed. [Up to 90 cm long but usually no more than 50 cm]

## Lemon sole - *Microstomus kitt*

Despite its name, the lemon sole is shaped like flatfish such as the plaice, flounder and dab (of which it is a relative) rather than having the characteristic rounded head of the sole (see below). Unlike all of these other flatfish, however, it is frequently seen on rocky seabeds such as here near St Abbs. Lemon soles often have an attractive and distinctive mottling pattern, which helps them to blend in with their surroundings. They feed on small rock-dwelling animals such as barnacles and chitons, and also on worms and the extended siphons of bivalve molluscs living in sand. [Up to 50 cm long]

## Sole - *Solea solea*

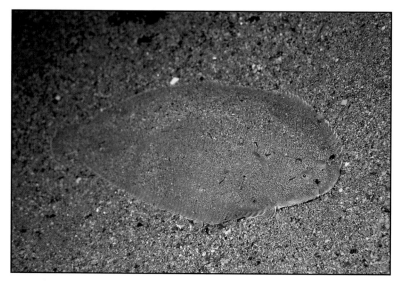

The sole (also known as the Dover sole) has a very characteristic rounded head, with a small curved mouth that is not positioned at the end of the snout as in most other flatfish. Its colour can vary from an even grey to a blotchy brown, depending on the seabed. The pectoral fin on its upper side, which has a black patch at its tip, can be held erect while the sole buries itself in the sand; it may mimic the dorsal fin of the poisonous weever fish (page 202) and so help to repel predators. Like the plaice and lemon sole, the sole's eyes are on what started out as the right-hand side of its body. [Up to 40 cm long]

# Topknot - *Zeugopterus punctatus*

The topknot is an unusual flatfish in that it is always found on rocky ground, unlike most species which live on sand or mud. It is also different from many flatfish in being "left-eyed," in that both eyes have ended up on what was originally the left side of the young fish. This separates it from the lemon sole which is also seen on rocky seabeds but is "right-eyed" like plaice, sole and most common flatfish. Topknots have a broad body with a fringing dorsal fin that starts right next to the snout. Colouration is usually brown with dark blotching, which provides excellent camouflage in the crevices where they tend to reside. With their habit of lying flat against the rock ceiling and staying put when approached, it may only be rippling fins or eyes glinting in a torch beam that give their presence away. A close look reveals that they have a dark blotch behind the pectoral fin in the middle of the body, and a broad dark stripe running outward from each eye. These markings distinguish *Zeugopterus punctatus* from the Norwegian topknot and Eckstrom's topknot, two similar but slightly smaller species. [Topknot up to 25 cm long]

# References for more information

The following publications were consulted during the writing of this book. I would recommend all of them for further reading.

Ager, O. E. D. (2001). *Funiculina quadrangularis*. The tall sea pen. Marine Life Information Network (www.marlin.ac.uk).

Alexander, R. McN. (1990). Animals. Cambridge University Press.

Angel, H. (1975). Seashore Life on Sandy Beaches. Jarrold.

Boycott, B. B. (1958). The Cuttlefish - *Sepia*. In: New Biology, volume 25. Penguin.

Buchsbaum, R., Buchsbaum, M., Pearse, J. & Pearse, V. (1987). Animals Without Backbones, third edition. The University of Chicago Press.

Burton, M. & Burton, R. (1975). Encyclopedia of Fish. Octopus Books.

Clarke, B. (2002). Good Fish Guide. Marine Conservation Society.

Daly, S. (1998). Marine Life of the Channel Islands. Kingdom Books.

Debelius, H. (1997). Mediterranean and Atlantic Fish Guide. IKAN.

Dipper, F. (2001). British Sea Fishes. Underwater World Publications.

Erwin, D. & Picton, B. (1987). Guide to Inshore Marine Life. Immel Publishing.

Fish, J. D. & Fish, S. (1996). A Student's Guide to the Seashore, second edition. Cambridge University Press.

Gibson, R., Hexstall, B. & Rogers, A. (2001). Photographic Guide to the Sea & Shore Life of Britain & North-west Europe. Oxford University Press.

Hanlon, R. T. & Messenger, J. B. (1988). Adaptive colouration in young cuttlefish: the morphology and development of body patterns and their relation to behaviour. Philosophical Transactions of the Royal Society. B, 320, 437-487.

Hawkins, S. J. & Jones, H. D. (1992). Marine Field Course Guide 1. Rocky Shores. Immel Publishing.

Hayward, P., Nelson-Smith, T. & Shields, C. (1996). Collins Pocket Guide. Sea Shore of Britain and Europe. Harper Collins Publishers.

Hayward, P. J. & Ryland, J. S. (1990). The Marine Fauna of the British Isles and North-West Europe. Oxford University Press.

Howson, C. M. & Picton, B.E. (eds) (1997). The species directory of the marine fauna and flora of the British Isles and surrounding seas. Ulster Museum and The Marine Conservation Society.

Ingle, R. W. (1980). British Crabs. Oxford University Press.

Ingle, R. W. (1992). Larval stages of Northeastern Atlantic crabs. Chapman and Hall.

Irving, R. (1998). Sussex Marine Life, an Identification Guide for Divers. East Sussex County Council.

Jackson, A. (2000). *Protanthea simplex*. Sealoch anemone. Marine Life Information Network (www.marlin.ac.uk).

Kershaw, D. R. (1988). Animal Diversity. Chapman and Hall.

Lythgoe, J. & Lythgoe, G. (1971). Fishes of the Sea. Blandford Press.

Manuel, R. L. (1988). British Anthozoa. The Linnean Society, E. J. Brill/Dr W. Backhuys.

Marshall, N. B. & Marshall, O. (1971). Ocean Life. Blandford Press.

Miller, S. A. & Harley, J. P. (1996). Zoology, third edition. Wm. C. Brown Publishers.

Muus, B. J. & Dahlstrom, P. (1974). Collins Guide to The Sea Fishes of Britain and North-Western Europe. Collins.

Picton, B. E. (1993). A Field Guide to the Shallow-water Echinoderms of the British Isles. Immel Publishing.

Picton, B. E. & Costello, M. J. (1998). The BioMAR biotope viewer: a guide to marine habitats, fauna and flora in Britain and Ireland, Environmental Sciences Unit, Trinity College, Dublin.

Picton, B. E. & Morrow, C. C. (1994). A Field Guide to the Nudibranchs of the British Isles. Immel Publishing.

Ruppert, E. E. & Barnes, R. D. (1994). Invertebrate Zoology, sixth edition. Saunders College Publishing.

Shick, J. M. (1991). A Functional Biology of Sea Anemones. Chapman and Hall.

Thompson, T. E. (1976). Biology of Opisthobranch Molluscs. The Ray Society.

Thompson, T. E. (1988). Molluscs: Benthic Opisthobranchs. The Linnean Society, E. J. Brill/Dr W. Backhuys.

Waller, G. (ed), Dando, M. & Burchett, M. (1996). Sealife, a Guide to the Marine Environment. Pica Press.

Warner, G. F. (1977). The Biology of Crabs. Paul Elek (Scientific Books).

Wilson, E. (1999). *Pachycerianthus multiplicatus*. Fireworks anemone. Marine Life Information Network (www.marlin.ac.uk).

Wood, E. (ed) (1988). Sea Life of Britain and Ireland. Immel Publishing.

Yonge, C. M. (1949). The Sea Shore. Collins.

Yonge, C. M. & Thompson T. E. (1976). Living Marine Molluscs. Collins.

Young, A. & Kay, P. (1994). Marine Wildlife of Atlantic Europe. Immel Publishing.

# Organisations promoting conservation and awareness of marine animals

The following organisations are all involved with these aims, and are good sources of information and inspiration. I am afraid it is not an exhaustive list:

The **Marine Conservation Society** is the UK's foremost charity dedicated to the protection of our marine environment and its wildlife. They work through campaigning, education and persuasion, always based on sound research; aiming to involve people in the care of the sea and its inhabitants. www.mcsuk.org

The **Wildlife Trusts** have launched a major UK campaign to help ensure a better future for the amazing wildlife that depends on our seas for survival. www.wildlifetrusts.org

The **Shark Trust** promotes the study, management and conservation of sharks, skates and rays. It collaborates with other members of the European Elasmobranch Association and aims to join forces with all those who want to ensure the future survival of these fascinating but vulnerable animals. www.sharktrust.org

**MarLIN** is the **Marine Life Information Network for Britain & Ireland**. It provides detailed, quality assured information to assist those engaged in environmental assessment, planning, response, site designation and management, education and recording. www.marlin.ac.uk

MarLIN is an initiative of the **Marine Biological Association of the United Kingdom** (MBA). The MBA is a professional body for marine scientists with world-wide membership. Its scientific staff undertake fundamental research in marine biology and it hosts the National Marine Biological Library. www.mba.ac.uk

The **Scottish Association for Marine Science** (SAMS) is a charity committed to promoting research and education in marine science. It has members from all over the world. www.sams.ac.uk

The **BioMar Biotope Viewer**: A guide to marine habitats, fauna and flora in Britain and Ireland. This contains a wealth of information on sites, habitats and species in the form of a map-linked database. www.itsligo.ie/biomar

The purpose of the **British Marine Life Study Society** is the study of the marine fauna and flora of the shore and seas surrounding the British Isles, the publication and distribution of knowledge and the promotion of ideas and projects concerning the conservation of the British marine environment. ourworld.compuserve.com/homepages/bmlss

**Torbay Coast and Countryside Trust's Seashore Centre** has interactive marine displays that show many interesting aspects of the intertidal zone, ranging from shells to plankton. A plankton guide can also be picked up at the Centre, which is at Tanners Road, Paignton, Devon. www.countryside-trust.org.uk

The **National Marine Aquarium**, in Plymouth, is a charity dedicated to increasing awareness and understanding of the oceans; the life they contain and man's interaction with them. Their aim is to entertain visitors while imparting an appreciation of water and the life it supports, through a series of stunning displays. www.national-aquarium.co.uk

**Sea Life** is committed to promoting education and awareness of our oceans. Visitors to Sea Life Centres can learn about environmental issues of concern, breeding programmes and the rescue and rehabilitation of sea creatures in distress. There are Centres at Birmingham, Blackpool, Bray, Brighton, Gt. Yarmouth, Hunstanton, Oban, Scarborough and Weymouth. www.sealife.co.uk

Other good places to learn about marine animals include:
**London Aquarium**. www.londonaquarium.co.uk
**The Deep**, Hull. www.thedeep.co.uk
**Deep Sea World**, North Queensferry, Fife. www.deepseaworld.co.uk
**Blue Planet Aquarium**, Ellesmere Port, Cheshire. www.blueplanetaquarium.com
**Lake District Coast Aquarium**, Maryport. www.lakedistrict-coastaquarium.co.uk
**Ilfracombe Aquarium**, Devon. www.ilfracombeaquarium.co.uk
**Blue Reef Aquarium**, Tynemouth, Portsmouth, Newquay. www.bluereefaquarium.com
**Macduff Marine Aquarium**, Banffshire. www.marine-aquarium.com
**Mallaig Marine World**. www.road-to-the-isles.org.uk/marine-world
**St David's Oceanarium**, Pembrokeshire. www.sealife.demon.co.uk
**Silent World Aquarium**, Tenby. www.jpmarketing.co.uk/silentworld
**Beaumaris Marine World**, Anglesey. www.beaumaris.org.uk
**Exploris Aquarium**, Portaferry. www.ards-council.gov.uk/exploris/exploris.htm
**Horniman Museum**, London. www.horniman.ac.uk
**National Lobster Hatchery**, Padstow, Cornwall. www.nationallobsterhatchery.com
**Sea Discovery Centre**, Axmouth, Devon. www.axcite.co.uk

**English Nature** (www.english-nature.org.uk), **Scottish Natural Heritage** (www.snh.org.uk) and the **Countryside Council for Wales** (www.ccw.gov.uk) are Government agencies that promote wildlife conservation. The **Joint Nature Conservation Committee** (JNCC) is the UK Government's wildlife adviser and works with these agencies. www.jncc.gov.uk

# Examples of different aspects of behaviour

This section lists a few species that give particularly good examples of the following types of behaviour.

## Co-operative or parasitic relationships between species

Rock cook cleaning ballan wrasse

| | Page |
|---|---|
| Snakelocks anemone and Leach's spider crab | 30, 88 |
| Parasitic anemone and common hermit crab | 40-41 |
| Cloak anemone and *Pagurus prideaux* (a hermit crab) | 42-43 |
| *Hydractinia echinata* (a hydroid) and hermit crabs | 56 |
| Compass jellyfish and lion's mane with young fish | 58-59 |
| Common prawn and conger eel | 99 |
| *Sacculina carcini* (a parasitic barnacle) and crabs | 103 |
| Queen scallop and sponge | 129 |
| Pollack and lamprey | 188-189 |
| Rock cook and ballan wrasse (and spider crab) | 206-207 (13) |

## Courtship and breeding*, including asexual reproduction

Courting cuttlefish

| | Page |
|---|---|
| Jewel anemone | 46-47 |
| Swimming crabs | 77-81 |
| Slipper limpet | 110 |
| Sea hare | 115 |
| Nudibranch sea slugs (various species) | 118-123 |
| Common cuttlefish | 132-133 |
| Common starfish | 147-148 |
| Lesser spotted dogfish | 178-179 |
| Pipefish | 194-195 |
| Lumpsucker | 199 |
| Corkwing wrasse | 209 |
| Viviparous blenny | 216 |
| Plaice | 221 |

* Typical jellyfish, crab and starfish life cycles are illustrated on pages 26, 76 and 142 respectively.

# Hunting and feeding
**Page**

Starfish feeding on a mussel bed

# Camouflage and defence
**Page**

Nudibranch sea slug gathering second-hand weapons

# Index of species, English and Latin names